THE BENTLEY COLLECTION GUIDE®

published by j.phillip, inc.

Fifth Edition
1997-1998

Acknowledgments

This book is dedicated to all who love and enjoy collecting the Longaberger Baskets®. Although these baskets are used for decorative and functional purposes, they have now been recognized for their collectibility. Special thanks to all who have helped contribute basket information, market values, and baskets for photography purposes. It is because of all of you that this Guide is the most comprehensive and accurate listing of Longaberger Products® available. A special thank you to our friend in Indiana who graciously opened her home to us for this Fifth Edition. We hope that your enthusiasm for the products comes through in every picture.

Please understand . . .

Photographs by: Andrew Korcok, Lighthouse Photo Services

Cover photos: Scenic, Ohio Statehouse Basket, Fellowship Basket™, scenic, J.W. Miniature Waste®, scenic, 97 Inaugural Tie-On, Feature Remembrance baskets, Charter Membership™ basket, Collectors Club™ Tie-On, scenic, Spirit of Longaberger®.

• 5870 Zarley Street - Suite C • New Albany, OH 43054-9700 •

• (800) 837-4394 • (614) 855-8507 •

• Email: Bentcol@aol.com • Website: http://www.bentleyguide.com •

ISBN 0-9646280-2-3

ISSN 1082-4790

Table of Contents

Letter from the Publisher

Dear Collector,

Welcome to the Fifth Edition of The Bentley Collection Guide®. We would like to thank all of you for your support and information that you have provided to us throughout the past five years. It is so exciting to us to reach our fifth anniversary and to celebrate, we feel that we are bringing you the ***best Bentley ever.*** All five of our editions have been made possible only through the generous input of many collectors throughout the market. Thank you for allowing us to bring this Fifth Edition to you.

The objective of this Guide is to provide a comprehensive and accurate listing of all baskets and products that have been produced by The Longaberger Company® of Dresden, Ohio. Although we are not affiliated with the company, our goal is to promote and further the collectibility of Longaberger Baskets®. Therefore, we have once again made several improvements to the Guide to provide more information and detail of the baskets:

First, we have corrected the confusion that surrounded the change in format with our Fourth Edition. After a couple of months of getting used to the changes, the range of values has been very well received as is apparent through many follow-up conversations and letters that we have received from several collectors in the market. There was an ongoing confusion with the absolute high occasionally being reported higher for the basket alone, compared to the combo or with accessories. Even though this does occasionally happen in the market, it is not a true reflection of the market. To help eliminate some of this confusion, we returned to reporting the High value as the *highest within the range of values we receive.* This change took effect with the Fourth Edition Six-Month Update and January 97 Pocket Guide. Please refer to page 6 in this introduction for a more complete explanation of these changes.

Other improvements include a new hole punch binding for The Bentley. This format will allow consultants to keep their Bentley right at their fingertips in their Longaberger Handbook™. Collectors can also benefit from the flexibility this binding offers by placing it in a Franklin Planner® or purchasing a Bentley binder to keep things organized. The checklist and hopefully the six-month update will also be available punched so you will no longer need to struggle to keep all of this information in one place.

As always, please keep in mind that the current market values listed in this book and in the Collector's Checklist should be used *only as a guide*. They are not intended to set prices, which vary from one section of the country to another. Secondary market prices vary greatly and are affected by many things, such as condition and demand. To better represent your specific market, we encourage you to report your results to us regularly.

We hope that you enjoy our Fifth Edition as much as we have enjoyed bringing it to you! May it bring you many hours of happy collecting!

History of The Longaberger Company®

In the early 1900's, in the small Ohio town of Dresden, John Wendell "J.W." Longaberger developed a love for hand-woven baskets. As a teenager, J.W. joined his father, Daddy John, at the Dresden Basket Company as a full-time basket weaver to help support the family. In 1927, J.W. married Bonnie Jean Gist and together they had 12 children. In order to support his large family, J.W. worked at the Dresden Paper Mill during the day, but continued to make baskets at night. In 1973, J.W. and his fifth child, Dave, began to teach others how to weave baskets. Although J.W. died that year, the quality and attention to detail that he wove into his baskets is kept alive, by Dave, through The Longaberger Company®.

Each basket is hand-woven, using hardwood maple splints. Since 1978, once a basket is completed it is dated and signed by the weaver. In 1982, the practice of burning The Longaberger® name and logo into the bottom of each basket began, guaranteeing its authenticity.

The company started selling through home parties in 1979. In 1981, the company had 100 consultants and delivery for baskets took approximately 8-12 weeks. Back then, the consultants delivered the orders to each hostess *personally*. Many changes have taken place since this humble beginning. Between 1995 and 1996, more than 12,000 consultants joined the Longaberger family. As of March 1997, The Longaberger Company® employs more than 5,000 people and produces over 150,000 baskets per week. There are approximately 36,000 sales consultants who sell Longaberger® products in all 50 states.

Achieving $500 Million in sales during November 1996, the company now estimates doubling this level in just four years. By the year 2000, they are targeting for $1 Billion in sales. Along with its growing popularity among collectors, The Longaberger Company® has also been recognized nationally for its dedication to quality and commitment to excellence by many major sources. Inc.® magazine recognized the company with their "Socially Responsible Entrepreneur" Award in 1992 and the U.S. Department of the Interior awarded the "Take Pride in America" Award to The Longaberger Company® in 1991.

The Longaberger Company® has come a long way from the home that once housed Dave's dream almost 20 years ago. We encourage you to visit Dresden, Ohio to fully catch the history and commitment behind this entrepreneurial vision. If you are interested in touring the Dresden area, call the Dresden Village Association at 1-800-315-1809 or The Longaberger Company® directly at 614-754-5000.

Purpose of this Guide

Interest in collecting Longaberger Baskets® and Pottery® has increased in recent years due to their increasing value, both inherently and monetarily. It no longer is surprising to see a collector basket double in value in only one year. Due to this interest, there is a need for reliable and accurate information about the value and identification of Longaberger Baskets® and Pottery®. As more Longaberger products® are produced, keeping this information updated is essential.

The purpose of The Bentley Collection Guide® is:

- To provide a reference tool to Secondary Market Dealers, Consultants, Collectors, Investors and Enthusiasts.

This is accomplished by:

- Providing actual selling (market) prices – not just "asking" prices.
- Lending credibility to Longaberger Baskets® and Pottery® as true collectibles.
- Providing a complete, up-to-date compilation of Longaberger® products, including individual pictures of products for identification purposes.
- Providing a "Quick Find" Index that also acts as a cross-reference of baskets made from the same form.
- Providing valuable information on how to identify and appraise Longaberger Products®.

There are many applications for this Guide, including:

- An essential educational manual for new, as well as experienced Consultants.
- A great training tool for Consultants on the history of Longaberger® products.
- A sales tool for Consultants to show customers that Longaberger® products have indeed increased in value.
- A price guide for those wanting to buy, sell, or trade baskets on the Secondary Market.
- An inventory checklist to record and price all of one's baskets.
- A reference tool for valuing one's baskets for insurance purposes.
- Identifying one's baskets and evaluating their condition.

Where to find Longaberger Baskets®

New Longaberger Baskets® can be obtained only through Sales Consultants, usually at a basket home party. The baskets are ordered from a Wish List™ containing products currently available directly from The Longaberger Company®. If you are interested in ordering a current line basket but do not know a Consultant, contact The Longaberger Company® at (800) 966-0374 to be directed to a Consultant in your area.

Collector and specialty baskets are available only for a limited time throughout the year. For example, the 1992 Christmas Collection Season's Greeting™ Basket was offered only from September through December of 1992. After this, the basket was no longer available from Longaberger®.

Older Longaberger Baskets® and Pottery® can be obtained only on the Secondary Market, which is made up of persons wanting to buy and sell these older products. These baskets are available from a number of sources. The directory on the next page is a listing of the various services we have found to be available for collectors to buy and sell their baskets.

Please understand . . .

The Directory of Secondary Market Resources on the next page is for **informational purposes only** and constitutes neither an endorsement nor a recommendation. The publisher does not assume any responsibility with regard to the selection, performance, or use of these services. All understandings, agreements, or warranties, if any, take place directly between the services and the prospective users. This listing of secondary market resources is based on information available at the time of publication and J. Phillip, Inc. makes no warranties as to the completeness or accuracy.

To help our customers better evaluate the services that are listed on the opposite page, we have devised a system to inform our customers of the length of our relationship with each service.

The 'β' listed to the right of each name represents the number of years that we have been in contact with the service.

It is not a rating system

We do not charge these services to be listed in this publication. The only requirement is that they have been in business for at least a year and consistently report their market results every month to us for at least a year. When dealing with any of these services, we do encourage you to let us know of your experience as we do wish to continue providing you with quality information about the secondary market.

Directory of Secondary Market Resources

Auctioneers: Auctions have been becoming a very popular way to buy or sell baskets within the last few years. Baskets can be purchased through the bidding process or can be put up for auction on a consignment basis. Each auctioneer has different terms and commission rates.

Craft & Michael Auctioneers, Inc. [β β β β β]

(219) 686-2615
or (219) 967-4442

P.O. Box 7
Camden, IN 46917

Brokers: Brokers will use a computerized system to match buyers and sellers throughout the country. There are usually fees involved once a match is made. Be sure to ask for a schedule of terms and fees before participating in this type of service.

The Basket Finder [β β]

Ask for Susan
(317) 473-7417

P.O. Box 1352
Peru, IN 46970-1352
Email: Basket4U@netusa1.net

Dealers: There are many dealers in the market that specialize in buying, selling or trading Longaberger Products®. This type of source is often preferred for collectors who have a need to acquire or liquidate items very quickly.

Baskets Galore [β β β β β]

(614) 453-9154
or (614) 453-8586

Zanesville, OH

Newsletters: Most newsletters are designed to bring basket lovers together by printing articles of interest. Some also have advertising sections for consultants and basket accessory crafters. The highlight of the newsletters is a section advertising baskets to buy, sell or trade.

The Basket Collector's Gazette [β β β β β]

(970) 641-3866

PO Box 322
Pitkin, CO 81241-0196

Newspapers & Magazine: The following sources have sections dedicated to advertising baskets to buy, sell, or trade. Most also have feature articles concerning The Longaberger Company® and other subjects of interest. It is not necessary to subscribe in order to advertise; however, some offer free space with a subscription.

Dresden Transcript [β β β β β]

(614) 754-1608

P.O. Box 105
Dresden, OH 43821-0105

Online / Internet: Here are some areas on the information supper highway that you may also find helpful.

Internet locations:	**American Online locations:**
http://www.bentleyguide.com	Bentcol@aol.com [mail only]
http://www.Longaberger.com	Keyword: Collectibles ->Other Collectibles -> List Topics [postboard]

About the Current Market Values

The prices provided in this Guide are Secondary Market values obtained from various sources, such as Dealers, Auctions, Collectors and Consultants.

The values shown are the *average* and the *highest* reported "selling price" for that particular basket, not the "asking" price. By providing the "selling" price of the baskets, the most accurate and reliable value is given for each basket. However, several points must be understood in relation to this pricing Guide:

(1) It is the intent of this Guide to gather all pricing data up to the last possible moment before the Guide is published. However, some prices may have changed due to the time it takes to publish and send this Guide. This is one reason for offering an update to this annual collector's guide; to keep the value of Longaberger® products continually up-to-date.

(2) The market values shown are not absolute. Increased demand in some areas may result in higher prices for particular baskets. It is also impossible to be aware of every sales transaction; therefore the market values listed may not be the absolute highest selling price during that particular period of time. We encourage you to help us represent your market even more accurately by reporting to us all transactions that you participate in throughout the year.

(3) Although some transactions reported to us may include shipping costs from seller to buyer, the prices reported in this Guide **do not include shipping and handling costs.** Even though shipping is often a part of a transaction, it is a cost of participating in the market and should not be considered part of a basket's value. However, you may need to consider this additional cost when insuring your collection because most insurance agency will only cover up to the insured value listed, regardless if there are additional costs incurred to replace the item.

(4) The range of values that are listed throughout the Guide reflect the range of activity that is occurring in the Secondary Market. The ***Average Value*** is determined by taking a straight average of the values reported and confirmed for an item during a specific period. The ***High Value*** is the highest value within the range of values reported. If a transaction is reported which we consider to be much higher than other results, we do not consider this to be a true reflection of the market and therefore will not report on it until more transactions in this area are reported. It is important to note that this definition of High is different from the one used in the Fourth Edition Guide, but is the same definition used in the first three editions.

Although this Guide and Collector's Checklist reflect what J. Phillip, Inc. considers to be current market values, J. Phillip, Inc. in no way warrants the prices listed therein. The publisher assumes no responsibility for any losses that might be incurred as a result of consulting this Guide.

The Bentley Collection Guide® is the most accurate and most reliable reference tool available for valuing Longaberger Products®.

Using this Guide

Finding your way through the Guide . . .

All collector edition and specialty baskets are listed categorically in the first part of this publication. The order of the categories is alphabetical and can be found in the Table of Contents. Regular Line baskets are not listed in the Guide, but are listed in the *Collector's Checklist* for inventory purposes. We do not include pictures of Regular Line baskets because we do not consider them a part of the secondary market since they are still available directly from the company. It is a good idea to keep a copy of a current Wish List™ with your Guide to have pictures of these baskets on hand.

The dimensions, form number and quantities produced are now listed directly under the picture. If it is not photographed, most of this information can be found in the *Quick Find*.

Reading the notations in the Guide . . .

Each basket in the Guide is listed by its year and name(s). Special characteristics may also be listed, such as "swinging" (sw/h) handles, "stationary" (st/h) handles, "no handles" (no/h), "inverted bottom", etc. If the basket was originally sold with accessories, the following notations will distinguish which accessories were available: Protector: **(P)**; Liner: **(L)**; Lid: **(Lid)**; Divider: **(Div)**.

If a basket was available as a Combo, the parenthesis that follows this notation will distinguish which items were originally a part of the Combo price. When many accessories were offered with a basket, the term "Full Set" has been created to reflect this combination selling in the market. The initials in parenthesis that follow will identify what we are considering a Full Set to include.

Applying the range of values to your collection . . .

After the description of the item, an original price, if available, is listed. The next two columns list the range of values from the current market. Before applying these values to your collection, it is important to fully understand how we are determining the Average and the High values throughout the Guide. These definitions can be found on page 6.

We consider the ***High Value*** to represent a basket in excellent condition while the ***Average Value*** better represents a more average product; however, without having seen each individual product, it is inappropriate for us to judge the condition of items reported to us. We encourage each collector to evaluate the condition of their individual collection before determining its market value. Refer to page 10 for help with valuing your collection.

When insuring your collection, the best option is to individually determine the unique value for each piece of your collection based on its demand, condition and other characteristics. If time is an issue, the ***High Value*** represents the potential of the collectible, thus should be used as the potential replacement cost.

Using this Guide

Dimensional Search . . .

On page 196, there is a reference tool that will help when trying to identify a basket by its dimensions. The baskets are divided into four size categories (square, rectangular, round, oval) and the dimensions are then listed in numerical order under each appropriate heading. The first page of this section lists specific steps to take when using this great tool to help identify items in your collection.

Quick Find Index . . .

The next section is a cross-reference index of baskets listed alphabetically by name, not collection. For example, *J.W. Corn*® is listed under *Corn* and then lists J.W. Collection® as a collection that this basket was available in. It will also list the other collections that have featured the Corn basket. This tool is great when wondering which collections a particular basket is available in or if the collector knows what the shape or form is, but is unsure of which collection it belongs. This index was specifically designed to be more helpful during auctions where a lot of information is needed quickly and when very little details of the item are made available to the collector. See page 137 for more information on how to use this section effectively.

Collector's Checklist . . .

The supplemental booklet that came with your Guide is an inventory checklist. The collector edition and specialty baskets are listed in the same manner as in the Guide. Regular Line baskets are listed alphabetically within the year they were offered.

This checklist enables you to indicate the quantity of baskets you may have, as well as your original cost. If a current market value has been reported, it is already printed on the checklist. The values listed are clarified by the following notations: C (Combos), B (basket only), L (basket sold with liner), or P (basket sold with protector). If any accessories were purchased with the baskets, such as liners or protectors, they can be noted in the description column. Any unique characteristics of the baskets should also be listed, such as special order color weave found in many earlier baskets.

When using the Checklist for insurance purposes, we do give permission to make one copy for your Insurance agent or to place in a safety deposit box. Additional copies are not permitted unless expressed written permission is given by J.Phillip, Inc.

A Word About Insurance

As your basket collection grows, you need to consider how best to cover it with insurance. A relatively small collection is usually not a problem under the normal homeowner's policy; however, any collection can be viewed as more than just a hobby if it reaches a size or falls into a category where the insurance company views it as more than "items normal and incidental to a normal household." A hobby can be viewed as a business, even though you have never sold one basket, simply because the potential to "some day" make money from it exists.

The best person to consult with on this is your insurance agent. He may initially recommend "scheduling" your individual baskets onto your policy, which simply means they are insured separately under a floater from the items listed as "unscheduled personal property" in your policy. If you don't schedule your baskets, at least make sure you have a "replacement cost endorsement" so that you will not have depreciation taken that you cannot recoup after a loss.

If you are an associate, you will need to have a separate business policy since your homeowner's has a limit on the amount they pay for business property. Your agent will be able to advise on the best package for covering your business risk. He also can explain some liability coverages. In today's "lawsuit happy world", even casual statements about "potential resale possibilities" or product durability can come back to haunt salespeople at some future date. Many have secured "professional liability" coverage to provide for defending themselves in court.

If you ever would suffer a smoke or fire loss, do not clean the baskets with normal household cleaners. Smoke has toxic chemicals that not only soil a basket, but interact with it chemically. It needs to be cleaned professionally, the sooner the better. After 24 hours, the damage begins to get substantially worse. Your insurance adjuster will not be upset if you have accrued some "reasonable expenses" to protect your baskets from further damage before he is able to inspect the loss. You will have saved him the cost of replacing them or at least improved their salvage value somewhat, even if they will not clean completely. Again, your agent can advise on who to call since he knows cleaning contractors who specialize in fire and smoke damage restoration.

Finally, as you should do with all your valuables, take photographs/videos in duplicate of each basket; identify it by noting type, age, unique characteristics, condition, original cost and current market value. Then keep a set of the photos/video at a location other than your house. Give the duplicates to your agent to keep in you file. Like any object, baskets get damaged and destroyed so you need to protect yourself from that potential loss, and insurance is a good start.

Richard Gordon, Jr.
Insurance Adjustor

The first step in identifying a Longaberger Basket® is to look on the bottom of the basket for the Longaberger® logo, which is burned into the basket. There have been five different logos used by the company since 1982:

Longaberger Stamp Progression:

Original stamp. First used in 1982 on the Grandad Sleigh, but broke in 1983. Prior to 1982, no stamp was used.

This stamp was a temporary replacement in 1983 and was used on several hundred baskets until it was replaced by a permanent one.

This was the third stamp, which started to be used in 1983. The company wanted the baskets to have Dresden Ohio on them, so it was replaced in 1989.

This stamp was only used for approximately one year, from 1989 to 1990. It was replaced with the fifth stamp.

This stamp was used from 1990 and is still being used currently.

However, if a basket does not have a logo, that does not mean it isn't a Longaberger Basket®. In this case, the basket was probably made before 1982. In addition, the weaver of the basket will usually initial the basket and date it. This practice began in 1978, when the company began selling the baskets through the home-party plan.

These are the three markings that help identify the authenticity of a Longaberger Basket®:

- **Longaberger Stamp – starting in 1982**
- **Date – starting in 1978**
- **Weaver's initials – also starting in 1978**

However, there are baskets produced by the company that may be missing any number of these marking, including all three. If your basket is missing any of these markings, we suggest having the basket authenticated directly by The Longaberger Company®. If you are not able to take it

(continued on page11)

(continued from page10)

to Dresden yourself, contact your Consultant and they may be able to help you make arrangements or give you instructions on how to ship it to the company for authentication.

In addition, baskets woven by J.W. himself, most likely will not have any markings on them. If you believe that a basket is an original J.W. basket (a basket hand-woven by J.W. himself), you will need to have it verified by one of the Longaberger family members. These baskets would have been made during the 1930s through the 1970s (before The Longaberger Company® began operations) and do have some identifying "trademarks" on them that were commonly found on J.W.'s work (see page 52). We are actively researching these baskets and hope to be able to bring you more information about them in future Bentley Guides.

The value of a basket will depend on several things:

• Is the basket part of a collection series or retired from the Regular Line?

Baskets which were part of a series, or were featured only for a short time, will generally be worth more than baskets still found in the Regular Line. A *collection series* is a series of baskets produced either on a yearly basis or for a limited time. There are different trends occurring in the market all of the time that will make different collections more "sought after". In the past year, some of the more popular series have been:

- Bob & Dolores Hope – page 119
- Collector's Club™ – page 31
- Incentive / Award baskets – page 75
- Traditions – page 129
- Employee baskets – page 47

• What year was the basket woven? Is the stain dark or is it light?

Baskets that were a part of the Regular Line, but later retired, tend to have higher values then those still in the Regular Line. However, older (darker stained) Regular Line baskets are beginning to become more popular. We have recently seen that collectors are starting to recognize the added value that these older baskets have due to their age as well as to the fact that they have a stain that is no longer available. If the older baskets have been maintained in good condition, they generally should be worth more than newer baskets for the following reasons: (1) There were fewer made each year, (2) older baskets have a darker stain, which

(continued on page12)

(continued from page11)

was discontinued in 1986, and (3) these baskets could be customized stained or unstained, with colored weaving and a variety of handles. These options are rarely ever offered anymore through the company.

• What is the condition of the basket?

The condition of a basket will significantly affect its value. A basket in "excellent" condition is worth much more than the same basket in "poor" condition. Determining the condition can be difficult to do and ultimately will need to be agreed upon by the buyer and seller. Keep in mind that these baskets are all handmade; thus some inconsistencies in weave or staining are natural to the process and add to the uniqueness of the product.

There are some characteristics, however, that should be considered not "natural" and may affect the value. Anything within the owner's control, such as, obvious heavy wear, broken handles, missing or cracked splints, or ink stained liners are just a few conditions that could lower the value of the basket.

• Is the basket signed by a family member?

Generally, baskets signed by members of the Longaberger® family can increase a basket's value, especially if the signature is either Dave's or Grandma Bonnie's. A collector can have their basket signed by taking it to Dresden or meeting up with the family at a Collectors Club™ event. In either case, it is getting more and more difficult to get signatures. The family has been cutting back due to many infringements of privacy that have occurred in the past year or two. Jerry Longaberger can still be found pretty easily in Dresden and is usually very happy to provide a signature. The other family members are a little more difficult to track down but are often available during the week of the Basket Bee™ in August. See page 94 later in the Guide for more information on the family members as well as pictures of actual signatures.

The value that a signature adds also depends on the circumstance surrounding the signature. For example, signatures on Bee™ baskets, Tour® baskets, Employee or Incentive baskets are more common because family members are more attainable during the Bee, in Dresden or to an employee. This does not mean that signatures on these baskets have no additional value, it just means that these signatures were theoretically easier to obtain.

Features:

Red & Blue Weave and Trim.

Photo		Description	MARKET VALUES Original	Avg.	High
A.	1987	Medium Berry™	19.95	**111**	**150**
B.	1987	Large Picnic™	64.95	**273**	**365**
C.	1988	Cake™	39.95	**127**	**180**
D.	1988	Small Picnic™	65.95	**178**	**225**
E.	1989	Stitching™	25.95	**119**	**155**
F.	1989	Quilting™	46.95	**165**	**210**
G.	1990	Small Spoon™	23.95	**88**	**110**
H.	1990	Medium Spoon™	27.95	**100**	**140**
I.	1990	Mini Waste™	35.95	**130**	**170**
J.	1990	Small Waste™	45.95	**138**	**200**
K.	1991	Two-Quart™	36.95	**110**	**140**
		Combo **(L)**	39.95	**110**	**155**
L.	1992	Small Market™	39.95	**112**	**165**
		with **P**rotector	48.90	**118**	**150**
		with **L**iner	56.90	**118**	**150**
		Combo **(P/L)**	54.95	**122**	**175**

The first year for the All-American Series was actually 1988, not 1987. The 1987 Medium Berry and Large Picnic were actually called the "Baskets and Stripes Forever" baskets. In 1988, the All-American Series was introduced and these baskets were then considered a part of the series.

A. 1987 Medium Berry

7.5^{L} x 7.5^{W} x 3.5^{H}

Form No: 1400-ABRS
No. Sold:

E. 1989 Stitching

7RD x 3^{H}

Form No: 5400-ABRS
No. Sold:

I. 1990 Mini Waste

7.5^{L} x 7.5^{W} x 10^{H}

Form No: 12000-OBRS
No. Sold:

Third in All-Around Basket Series

B. 1987 Large Picnic

17^{L} x 14^{W} x 11^{H}

Form No: 300-HBRS
No. Sold:

Hostess only

C. 1988 Cake

12^{L} x 12^{W} x 6^{H}

Form No: 100-GBRS
No. Sold:

Divider shelf also came with the basket.

D. 1988 Small Picnic

12^{L} x 12^{W} x 6^{H}

Form No: 100-HBRS
No. Sold:

Hostess only

F. 1989 Quilting

12RD x 5.75^{H}

Form No: 54000-ABRS
No. Sold:

Hostess only

G. 1990 Small Spoon

5.5^{L} x 5.5^{W} x 6^{H}

Form No: 10000-OBRS
No. Sold:

First in All-Around Basket Series

H. 1990 Medium Spoon

6.5^{L} x 6.5^{W} x 8^{H}

Form No: 11000-OBRS
No. Sold:

Second in All-Around Basket Series

J. 1990 Small Waste

9.5^{L} x 9.5^{W} x 12^{H}

Form No: 1800-OBRS
No. Sold:

Hostess only. Fourth in All-Around Basket Series.

K. 1991 Two-Quart

9.5^{L} x 5^{W} x 9.5^{H}

Form No: 1000-CBRS
No. Sold:

L. 1992 Small Market

15^{L} x 9.5^{W} x 5.5^{H}

Form No: 10707
No. Sold:

Features:

This series is usually promoted during June.

M. 1993 Liberty
11.5^L x 5^W x 3^H
Form No: 14541
No. Sold:

Photo		Description	Original	Avg.	High
M.	1993	Liberty™	29.95	**59**	**75**
		with **P**rotector	33.90	**59**	**83**
		with **L**iner	37.90	**64**	**83**
		Combo **(P/L)**	36.95	**70**	**95**
N.	1994	Candle™	34.95	**63**	**80**
		with **P**rotector	39.90	**65**	**80**
		with **L**iner	47.90	**65**	**80**
		Combo **(P/L)**	42.95	**70**	**85**
O.	1995	Carry-Along™	34.95	**63**	**87**
		with **P**rotector	39.90	**63**	**90**
		with **L**iner	48.90	**63**	**90**
		Combo **(P/L)**	44.95	**67**	**100**
O.	1995	Flag Tie-On	6.95	**17**	**20**
P.	1996	Summertime™	34.95	**60**	**65**
		with **P**rotector	39.90	**53**	**65**
		with **L**iner	47.90	**53**	**65**
		Combo **(P/L)**	44.95	**60**	**75**
P.	1996	Small Flag Tie-On	5.95	**9**	**11**
Q.	1997	Patriot™	32.95	—	—
		with **P**rotector	36.90	—	—
		with **L**iner	44.90	—	—
		Combo **(P/L)**	44.95	—	—
		with **Lid**	47.90	—	—
		Full Set **(Combo/Lid)**	59.90	—	—

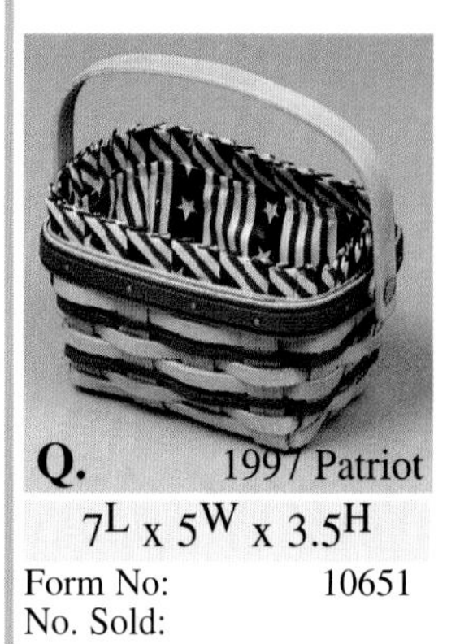

Q. 1997 Patriot
7^L x 5^W x 3.5^H
Form No: 10651
No. Sold:

• *Basket Fun Facts* •

The "All-Around Basket Series" was a campaign in June 1990. These baskets were available with show dates from June 1 through June 30, 1990. The focus of this campaign was "Keep America Beautiful", so the Spoon and Waste Basket forms were chosen as the feature.

N. 1994 Candle

$9^L \times 5^W \times 5^H$

Form No: 11134
No. Sold:

O. 1995 Carry-Along

$5.5^L \times 5.5^W \times 6^H$

Form No: 14656
Tie-On: 31551
No. Sold:

Tie-On sold separately

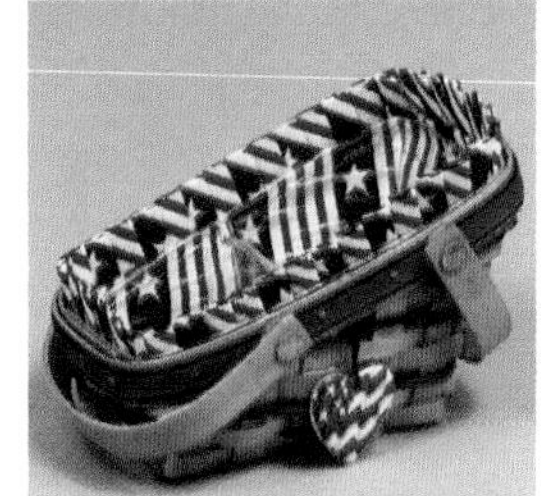

P. 1996 Summertime

$7.75^L \times 4.5^W \times 2.25^{FH} \times 4.5^{BH}$

Form No: 18911
Tie-On: 32891
No. Sold:

Combo came with a divided protector. A regular protector was also offered for an additional $3.95. Tie-On sold separately.

• Market Fun Facts •

;oing trend in the Secondary Market has been seen with the popularity of signatures. past year, we have been able to confirm that signatures do indeed add to the value of a but the question is still "How much?". It really depends on the signature, the number atures and the circumstance surrounding the signature. Grandma Bonnie and Dave ie to be the highest valued signature in the market. Dave has been known to even be pted during his lunch at Popeye's to sign for a Dresden visitor. However, due to nfringements on privacy, the family has been cutting back on signings. Bee attendees) finding it harder to "snag" a family member. During the past couple Bees, the com- as resulted to allowing only a few lucky Bee attendees to have baskets signed through y process. This means that signatures are becoming harder and harder to get.

to the excitement of signatures in the market, The Company started a new tradition h of this year. Jerry, Wendy, Judy, Ginny Lou and occasionally Grandma Bonnie will ing ***regular line*** baskets to send out with random shows. Not only does this do a ob of bringing a little bit of Dresden to far away cities, but it could also help to increase ie of those current regular line baskets. How much? It will depend on your market demand for signatures there.

• Basket Fun Facts •

The Longaberger Company® offers many incentives throughout the year to motivate their Advisors. Free products, free promotional materials and free samples are very common motivators for the sales force. Since 1992, The Company has also offered incentive trips for what is referred to as the "Top 10 Point Earners".

While the goals may be different each year, the concept has stayed the same. The home office determines certain criteria and levels of achievement and then attach points to each level. As the Consultants sell, they are earning points towards a trip. Those who earn 2000 points are able to go on the trip at no cost. If they are able to earn 1600 points, the company does allow them to "buy" the remaining points to be able to go. A maximum of two trips may be earned to allow the Consultants to take their spouse or friend.

1992:

5^L x 5^W x 2.5^H

"Fantasy in Paradise"

This basket was given to top achievers on a trip to the Bahamas.

1993:

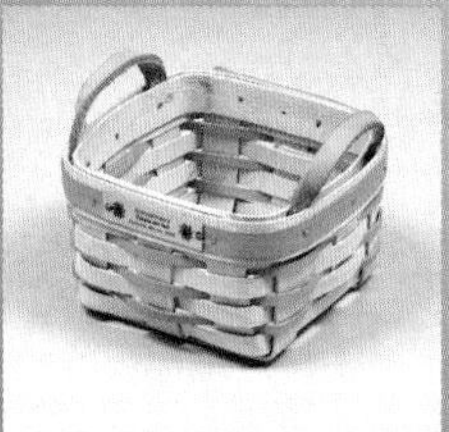

5^L x 5^W x 2.5^H

"Fiesta del Sol"

During a trip to Cancun, top point earners were recognized with this basket.

1994:

This year, the trip was a "Hawaiian Holiday". Baskets were not given to attendees.

1995:

A Royal Caribbean cruise, "Ports of Paradise", was the goal this fourth year. Two trips were planned so that everyone who went could have a cabin facing the outside of the ship. No baskets were given, but everyone did receive an engraved captain's clock.

1996:

Last year, "Sunsational Celebration" was the theme and the trip was again to the Bahamas. 1050 Advisors and guests attended. For the first time, the Top 12 Point Earners were treated to a separate trip to New York City to launch the festivities. To our knowledge, no baskets were given.

Bee Baskets™

Features:

Only available to those who attend the Basket Bee™.
Starting in 1990, tagged with Bee Theme.

Photo		Description	Original	Avg.	High
	1988	Bee Decorated Basket Contest			
A.		Small Peg	N/C	—	—
		Medium Peg [np]	N/C	—	—
		Large Peg [np]	N/C	—	—
B.	1988	Large Bee Basket™		145	165
	1988	Medium Bee Basket™		—	—
C.	1989	Bee Basket™		145	180
D.	1990	Bee Basket™	19.90	85	95
E.	1991	Bee Basket™	19.91	81	120
F.	1992	Bee Basket™	20.00	89	110
G.	1993	Bee Basket™	25.00	100	125
		with **P**rotector		106	130
		with **L**iner		106	130
		Combo **(P/L)**		115	150
G.		with Tote	N/C	—	—
H.	1994	Bee Basket™	25.00	206	325
		with **P**rotector		206	325
		with **L**iner		206	325
		Combo **(P/L)**		206	325
H.		with Tote	N/C	—	—
H.	1994	Bee Tie-On™		—	—

About The Bee™ . . .

This celebration of baskets is not for the faint of heart. "Dresden Days" are usually held the last day of each Bee™. On these days, vendors from all over the country set up tables throughout Dresden and the town is flooded with enthusiasts from all states. The 1997 Bee™ is called the "Bringing America Home" Bee™ and will be held on 7/30 - 8/2, 8/3 - 8/6, and 8/6 - 8/9.

Hope to see you there!

KEY: [np] = Not Pictured

The Basket Bee™ is the annual convention, usually in August, that The Company hosts in Columbus, Ohio for their Consultants. The first year for "The Bee" was 1981. Now, "The Bee" has grown to <u>three</u> conventions, each consisting of three days of speakers and seminars and one day to visit Dresden.

B. 1988

14^L x 7.75^W x 5.25^H

Form No: 3600-AO
No. Sold:

No Tag. Stained over Medium AND Large Easter baskets. Available with Blue, Green, Lilac, or Pink weaving.

E. 1991

8.5^L x 8.5^W x 5^H

Form No: 1500-
No. Sold:

Teal and burgundy weave. Theme: "Imagine the Possibilities"

"Proud To Be Me"

1985 (Potpourri)

$5^L \times 5^W \times 2.5^H$

"Our Country Feeling"

1986 (Forget-Me-Not)

$5^{RD} \times 4.5^H$

The 1985 and 1986 Bee Baskets shown above were not officially given out by The Longaberger Company®. These baskets were Booking Baskets tagged by various Directors for their consultants. The first Bee Basket sponsored by the company was in 1988, in which Large and Medium Easter baskets were stained over.

A. Decorated 1988 Small Peg

$5^L \times 5^W \times 4.5^H$

Form No: 14000-AO
No. Sold:

Med.Peg: $5.5^L \times 5.5^W \times 6^H$
Lg. Peg: $6.5^L \times 6.5^W \times 8^H$

C. 1989

$8.75^L \times 4.75^W \times 6.5^H$

Form No: 5600-BRST
No. Sold:

Christmas Memory, including Christmas tag. Only difference is wooden bottom

C. 1989 wooden bottom

Bee Theme burned into bottom. Theme: "Weave Your American Dream"

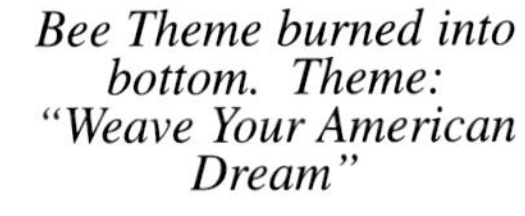

D. 1990

$7^{RD} \times 6.5^H$

Form No: 3900-AO
No. Sold:

Dusty rose and blue weave. Theme: "Together We're on the Move".

F. 1992

$14^L \times 9^W \times 4.5^H$

Form No: 12335
No. Sold:

Burgundy, teal and golden rod weave. Theme: "Discover the Vision"

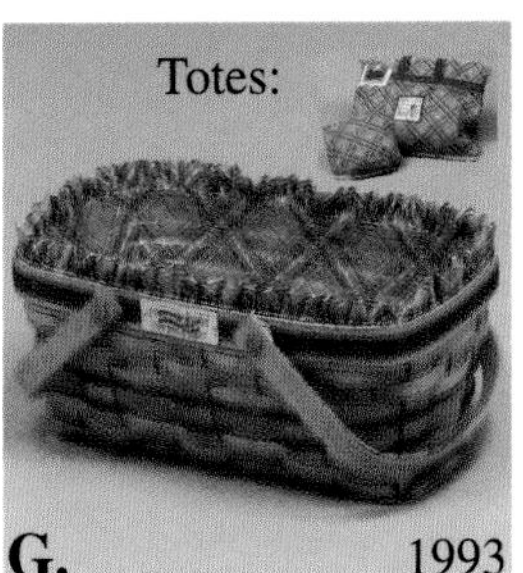

Totes:

G. 1993

$13^L \times 8^W \times 5^H$

Form No: 13501
No. Sold:

Pink and teal weave. Theme: "Making it Happen Together" First year for accessories.

Totes:

H. 1994

$6.5^L \times 6.5^W \times 8^H$

Form No: unknown
No. Sold:

Rose pink and purple weave. Theme: "Celebrate Your Success".

Features:

Only available to those who attend the Basket Bee™. Starting in 1990, tagged with Bee Theme.

Photo		Description	Original	Avg.	High
			MARKET VALUES		
I.	1995	Bee Basket™	25.00	**190**	**250**
		with **P**rotector	29.95	**190**	**250**
		with **L**iner	37.95	**190**	**250**
		Combo **(P/L)**	42.90	**190**	**275**
I.		with Tote	N/C	—	—
I.	1995	Bee Tie-On™		—	—
J.	1996	Bee Basket™	25.00	**131**	**200**
		with **P**rotector	29.95	**131**	**200**
		with **L**iner	37.95	**131**	**200**
		Combo **(P/L)**	42.90	**135**	**250**
		with Tote	N/C	—	—
J.	1996	Bee Tie-On™		—	—

I. 1995

10^L x 6^W x 4^H

Form No: unknown
No. Sold:

Purple and green weave. Theme: "It Begins with a Dream" Accessories sold separately.

J. 1996

8.5^L x 8.5^W x 5^H

Form No: unknown
No. Sold:

Gold, red and blue weave. Theme: "Light the Fire Within" Accessories sold separately.

• *Bee™ Fun Facts* •

Starting in 1995, even the local Dresden Post Office decided to become a part of The Bee™ spirit. When collectors brought their prestamped mailings (or baskets) with them during the Bee™, the Post Office would hand stamp the pieces with these commemorative Bee cancellation stamps.

1995

1996

BOOKING / PROMO BASKETS

Features:

Available *free* to Hostesses for achieving certain goals.
No color.
Prior to 1990: 1/2" weave. After 1990: 3/8" weave.

Photo	Description		Original	Avg.	High
A.	1980	Sunburst	3.95	**115**	**150**
	19XX-84	Small Spoon [WL]	—	**—**	**—**
		5" Measuring [WL]	—	**—**	**—**
		Button [WL]	6.43	**—**	**—**
B.	1984-90	Candle™	—	**65**	**100**
C.	1985-90	Potpourri™	3.00	**55**	**80**
D.	1986-87	Forget-Me-Not™	—	**55**	**85**
E.	1988	Sugar and Spice™	—	**57**	**75**
F.	1988-90	Keepsake™	16.95*	**50**	**75**
G.	1990-92	Ivy™	**	**50**	**65**
		with **P**rotector	2.95	**52**	**67**
H.	1990-92	Laurel™	**	**48**	**70**
		with **P**rotector	2.95	**48**	**70**
I.	1990-92	Rosemary™	**	**56**	**60**
		with **P**rotector	2.95	**56**	**70**
J.	1992-94	Sweet Basil™	22.95*	**40**	**60**
		with **P**rotector	25.90	**42**	**63**
		with **L**iner	31.90	**42**	**63**
		Combo **(P/L)**	34.85	**48**	**65**
K.	1992-96	Ambrosia™	22.95*	**39**	**55**
		with **P**rotector	25.90	**39**	**55**
		with **L**iner	31.90	**39**	**55**
		Combo **(P/L)**	34.85	**46**	**60**
L.	1992-95	Potpourri Sachet	11.95*	**—**	**—**

KEY

*Basket Value, not cost.

***Free*, with 2+ bookings

[WL] = *Wish List*™. It is similar to what is available today. Pictures can be found in a current *Wish List*™. See the *Quick Find* for dimensions and form numbers.

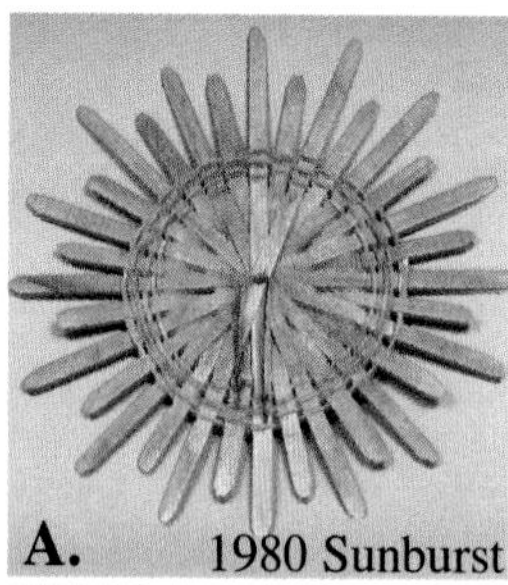

A. 1980 Sunburst

22" diameter

Form No: 7000-O
No. Sold:

E. 1988 Sugar and Spice

5.75L x 3.75W x 3H

Form No: 45000-AO
No. Sold:

I. 1990-92 Rosemary

5.75L x 3.75W x 3H

Form No: 45000-JOS
No. Sold:

3/8" Weave. Free to Hostesses with 2+ Bookings.

B. 1984-90 Candle

$9^{L} \times 5^{W} \times 5^{H}$

Form No: 1100-AO
No. Sold:

C. 1985-90 Potpourri

$5^{L} \times 5^{W} \times 2.5^{H}$

Form No: 13000-AO
No. Sold:

Free to Hostesses with show sales greater than $150.

D. 1986-87 Forget-Me-Not

$5^{RD} \times 4.5^{H}$

Form No: 3800-AO
No. Sold:

Free to Hostesses with show sales greater than $150.

F. 1988-90 Keepsake

$5.75^{L} \times 3.75^{W} \times 3^{H}$

Form No: 45000-IO
No. Sold:

G. 1990-92 Ivy

$5.5^{L} \times 5.5^{W} \times 2.5^{H}$

Form No: 13100-JOS
No. Sold:

3/8" Weave. Free to Hostesses with 2+ Bookings.

H. 1990-92 Laurel

$5.5^{RD} \times 3.75^{H}$

Form No: 17000-JOS
No. Sold:

3/8" Weave. Free to Hostesses with 2+ Bookings.

J. 1992-94 Sweet Basil

$5^{L} \times 5^{W} \times 2.5^{H}$

Form No: 10146
No. Sold:

3/8" Weave. Free to Hostesses with 2+ Bookings.

K. 1992-96 Ambrosia

$5.5^{L} \times 4^{W} \times 4^{H}$

Form No: 10120
No. Sold:

3/8" Weave. Free to Hostesses with 2+ Bookings.

L. 1992-95 Sachet

N/A

Form No: 209581
No. Sold:

Free with 1 Booking.

• We Need You •

Most of the research information we obtain comes from Consultants and Collectors, just like yourself. We are constantly calling your ads that have been placed in certain forums like the *Dresden Transcript, Collectors Exchange*, or *The Basket Collector's Gazette* to confirm actual selling prices. You may have been called yourself and have already volunteered your information. If you have, **THANK YOU VERY MUCH!**

For those who have not been contacted yet, it is probably because we either do not know about your ad or have not had a chance to call on your ad.

DON'T BE MISSED

Whenever you **buy, sell, or trade** any Longaberger Products® on the Secondary Market, you can call us or send us your results:

Here's how:

1. **CALL or FAX us at 1-800-VERIFY IT (800-837-4394)**
   Monday through Friday from 9:00am – 5:00pm (EST) – Ask for the Research Dept.
2. **EMAIL us at Bentcol@aol.com**
   Website: http://www.bentleyguide.com
3. **MAIL your results to: 5870 Zarley Street, Suite C**
   New Albany, OH 43054-9700

Here's the Information we need to Know:

- Name of Basket and the Collection to which it belongs.
- Year
- Buy, sell or trade?
- Selling price (not including shipping)
- Condition
- Accessories (liner, protector, tie-on, combo, lid, divider, etc . . .)
- Signatures (who and how many)
- What forum in the industry was used to make the transaction (internet, newspaper, newsletter, auction, word of mouth, etc . . .)
- What state was the transaction made (selling state and buying state)

Even if you bought or sold below "Bentley prices", your information is still ***very important and essential****. It will add to the accuracy of the Guide and represent your area of the country better.* ***Call us with your results!***

BASKETS

Features:

Red or Green Weave and Trim.
Commemorative Brass Tag.

Photo	Description			Original	Avg.	High
				MARKET VALUES		
A.	1981	Candle™		14.95	**600**	**850**
B.	1982	Grandad Sleigh™		19.95	**720**	**850**
C.	1983	Bell™		22.95	**615**	**750**
D.	1984	Holly™		24.95	**320**	**390**
E.	1985	Cookie™		24.95	**211**	**280**
			with Liner	33.95	**243**	**300**
F.	1986	Candy Cane™		26.95	**180**	**280**
G.	1987	Mistletoe™		19.95	**115**	**180**
H.	1988	Poinsettia™		26.95	**102**	**155**
I.	1989	Memory™		34.95	**86**	**135**
J.	1990	Gingerbread™		32.95	**95**	**130**
			with **P**rotector	37.90	**105**	**130**
			with **L**iner	45.90	**105**	**130**
			Combo **(P/L)**	50.85	**110**	**135**
K.	1991	Yuletide Traditions™		38.95	**92**	**130**
			with **P**rotector	45.90	**104**	**135**
			with **L**iner	52.90	**104**	**135**
			Combo **(P/L)**	59.85	**110**	**140**
L.	1992	Season's Greetings™		44.95	**87**	**125**
			with **P**rotector	49.90	**89**	**125**
			with **L**iner	57.90	**89**	**125**
			Combo **(P/L)**	53.95	**92**	**130**

KEY

* = Substitute **R** for Red or **G** for Green.

† = Product numbers are stated Red weave / Green weave.

A. 1981 Candle

$9^L \times 5^W \times 5^H$

Form No: 1100-
No. Sold: 2,000

E. 1985 Cookie

$7^{RD} \times 3^H$

Form No: 5400-A*
No. Sold:

First Christmas basket offered with an accessory. Liners were not offered again until 1990.

I. 1989 Memory

$8.75^L \times 4.75^W \times 6.5^H$

Form No: 5600-B*ST
No. Sold: 129,651

B. 1982 Grandad Sleigh

9.25^{L} x 5.5^{W} x 2^{FH} x 5.5^{BH}

Form No: 4900-Z
No. Sold: 3,200

Available with red tag only. Grandad with one 'd' was an intentional misspelling.

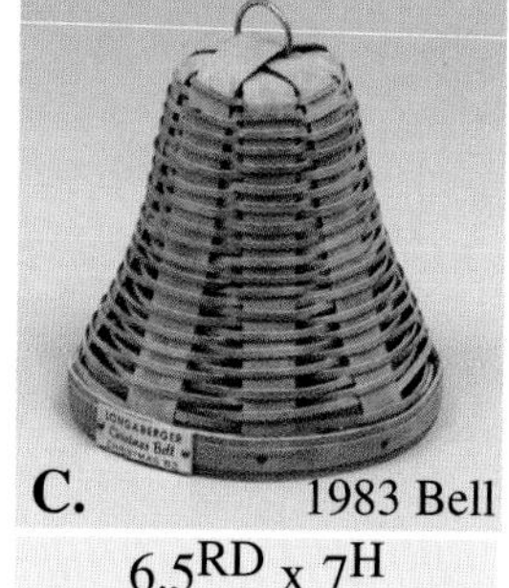

C. 1983 Bell

6.5^{RD} x 7^{H}

Form No: 4901-OO
No. Sold: 3,700

Available with red or green tag.

D. 1984 Holly

15^{L} x 8^{W} x 2.25^{H}

Form No: 4600-AZ
No. Sold: 16,494

Only available in red.

F. 1986 Candy Cane

5^{L} x 5^{W} x 4.5^{H}

Form No: 14000-A*T
No. Sold:

G. 1987 Mistletoe

7^{L} x 5^{W} x 3.5^{H}

Form No: 700-A*T
No. Sold:

H. 1988 Poinsettia

7RD x 6.5^{H}

Form No: 3900-B*ST
No. Sold:

J. 1990 Gingerbread

10^{L} x 6^{W} x 4^{H}

Form No: 3400-A*ST
No. Sold: 165,117

First year both liner and protector offered with basket.

K. 1991 Yuletide Traditions

13^{L} x 7.5^{W} x 3^{FH} x 8^{BH}

Form No: 5100-C*ST
No. Sold: 147,247

L. 1992 Season's Greetings

9.5^{L} x 6^{W} x 6^{H}

Form No: 10316/10219†
No. Sold:

Features:

Red or Green Weave and Trim.
Commemorative Brass Tag.

Photo	Description	Original	Avg.	High
M.	1993 Bayberry™	42.95	**73**	**115**
	with **P**rotector	48.90	**78**	**125**
	with **L**iner	55.90	**78**	**125**
	Combo **(P/L)**	49.95	**82**	**140**
N.	1994 Jingle Bell ™	47.95	**77**	**95**
	with **P**rotector	54.90	**78**	**100**
	with **L**iner	62.90	**78**	**100**
	Combo **(P/L)**	59.95	**90**	**125**
	with **Lid**	67.90	—	—
	Full Set (**Combo/Lid**)	79.90	**105**	**140**
N.	1994 Jingle Bell Tie-On	6.95	**11**	**18**
O.	1995 Cranberry™	47.95	**78**	**90**
	with **P**rotector	54.90	**80**	**90**
	with **L**iner	64.90	**80**	**90**
	Combo **(P/L)**	59.95	**90**	**110**
	with **Lid**	67.90	—	—
	Full Set (**Combo/Lid**)	79.90	**95**	**110**
O.	1995 Merry Christmas Tie-On	6.95	**13**	**17**
	1995 Happy Hanukkah Tie-On [np]	6.95	—	—
	1995 Apron [np]	24.95	—	—
P.	1996 Holiday Cheer ™	47.95	**60**	**70**
	with **P**rotector	53.90	—	—
	with **L**iner	64.90	—	—
	Combo **(P/L)**	59.95	**70**	**88**
	with **Lid**	69.90	—	—
	Full Set (**Combo/Lid**)	81.90	—	—
	1996 Merry Christmas Tie-On	6.95	—	—

(MARKET VALUES: Original, Avg., High)

M. 1993 Bayberry

9^L x 9^W x 4.5^H

Form No: 11584/11592†
No. Sold:

N. 1994 Jingle Bell

8RD x 6^H

Form No: 17906/17914†
Tie-On: 31437
No. Sold:

Tie-On and Lid not included in Combo.

KEY

† = Product numbers are stated: **Red** weave / **Green** weave.

[np] = Not Pictured.

O. 1995 Cranberry

8.5^L x 8.5^W x 7^H

Form No: 19500/19518†
Tie-On: 32441
No. Sold:

Tie-On and Lid not included in Combo.

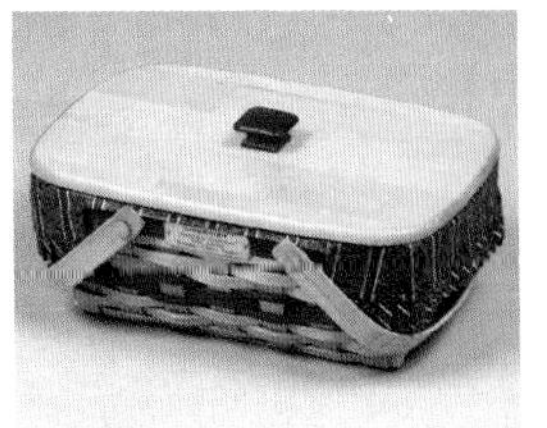

P. 1996 Holiday Cheer

12^L x 8^W x 4.25^H

Form No: 18520/18511†
Tie-On: 31704
No. Sold:

Tie-On and Lid not included in Combo.

Collectors Club™

Features:

J.W.® Blue and Traditions™ Green Trim and Weave. Commemorative brass tag.

MARKET VALUES

Photo		Description	Original	Avg.	High
		1996 Items:			
A.	1995-96	Charter Membership	75.00	**105**	**135**
		with **P**rotector	83.95	—	—
		with **L**iner	94.95	—	—
		Combo **(P/L)**	103.90	**158**	**230**
B.	1996	Miniature J.W. Market®	125.00	**192**	**250**
		with **P**rotector	127.95	**200**	**250**
		with **L**iner	138.95	**200**	**250**
		Combo **(P/L)**	141.90	**232**	**310**
C.	1996	Membership Tie-On	N/C	**55**	**70**
D.	1996	Small Serving Tray	69.95	**175**	**185**
		with **P**rotector	79.90	—	—
		with **L**iner	92.90	—	—
		Combo **(P/L)**	102.85	**175**	**200**
E.	1996	Longaberger University Ornament	29.95	**45**	**65**
		1997 Items:			
	1997	1st Yr Membership[np]	75.00	—	—
		with **P**rotector	83.95	—	—
		with **L**iner	94.95	—	—
		Combo **(P/L)**	103.90	—	—
F.	1997	Renewal Basket™	39.95	—	—
		with **P**rotector	44.90	—	—
		with **L**iner	54.90	—	—
		Combo **(P/L)**	59.85	—	—
G.	1997	Miniature J.W. Waste®	99.95	—	—
		with **P**rotector	102.90	—	—
		with **L**iner	113.90	—	—
		Combo **(P/L)**	116.85	—	—

A. 1996 Membership

9.5^{L} x 5^{W} x 9.5^{H}

Form No: 62839
No. Sold:

Top half of basket woven with 1/2: weaving, while a 3/8" weave was used on the bottom half. Box included.

E. 1996 Ornament

3.5^{RD}

Form No: 33758
No. Sold:

KEY: [np] = Not Pictured

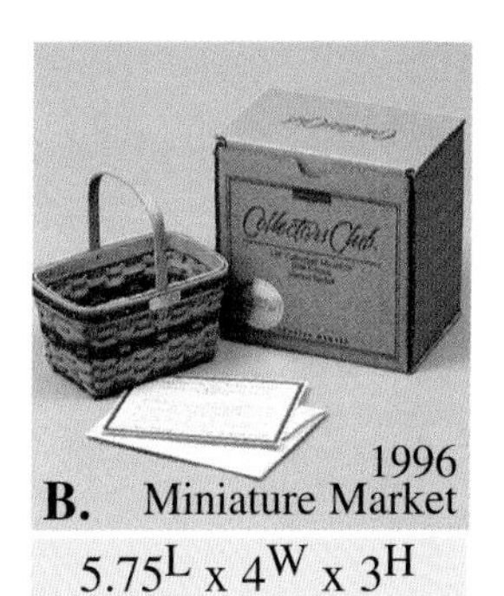

B. 1996 Miniature Market

$5.75^{L} \times 4^{W} \times 3^{H}$

Form No: 150240
Signed: 15024
No. Sold:

Accessories sold seperately. Seal on the box designates the basket was signed by a family member.

C. 1996 Membership Tie-On

$2.5^{W} \times 1.75^{H}$

Form No: 83089
No. Given: ≈ 95,000

D. 1996 Serving Tray

$11.5^{L} \times 15.5^{W} \times 3.75^{H}$

Form No: 12629
No. Given:

F. 1997 Renewal

$9^{L} \times 5^{W} \times 5^{H}$

Form No: 105702
No. Sold:

G. 1997 Miniature Waste

$3.75^{L} \times 3.75^{W} \times 4.75^{H}$

Form No: 17797
No. Sold:

About the Collectors Club™ . . .

The Longaberger Company® first started the Collectors Club™ in December 1995. This Club acknowledges the Secondary Market and the collectibility of The Longaberger Baskets® and Products®. Its purpose is to bring Longaberger Collectors together to share ideas, have a chance to purchase exclusive products, receive product insight, hear stories of other Collectors throughout the country through a quarterly magazine, *Signatures*™, and stay in touch with the Secondary Market via a monthly issue, *Collectors Exchange*™, set up to advertise baskets and products.

• Basket Fun Facts •

The Spirit of Longaberger™

This annual award is possibly the most prestigious award that The Longaberger Company® gives. It is an award to recognize the "Achievements of The Heart".

There are eight different criterion set for the award and each candidate is nominated by their peers. Nominations are usually accepted until the end of May and the award is given to one person at each Bee™. The first award was given in 1994. At the 1997 Bee™, award number nine, ten and eleven will be handed out.

Areas of Achievement:

- ***a sense of family***
- ***sharing, caring and helping others***
- ***treating others the way they want to be treated***
- ***humor, the ability to laugh at one's self***
- ***the pursuit of excellence***
- ***a commitment to education, recreation and community beyond what is typically expected***
- ***a concern for the environment***
- ***an active pursuit of human endeavors aimed at stimulating a better quality of life***

Cookie Molds

COOKIE MOLDS

Features:
Santa Series: 1990 – 1993
Angel Series: 1993 – 1996
Easter Series: 1994 – 1997
Gingerbread Series: 1995 – present

MARKET VALUES

Photo	Description	Original	Avg.	High
	Santa Series™			
A.	1990 Father Christmas™	18.95	**62**	**125**
B.	1990 1st Casting™	18.95	**102**	**150**
C.	1991 Kriss Kringle™	18.95	**30**	**75**
D.	1992 Santa Claus™	18.95	**30**	**50**
E.	1993 St.Nick™	18.95	**34**	**45**
	Santa Series Full Set of 4		**165**	**200**
	Angel Series™			
F.	1993 Peace™	18.95	**33**	**50**
G.	1994 Hope™	19.95	**24**	**40**
H.	1995 Love™	19.95	**25**	**35**
I.	1996 Joy™	19.95	**—**	**—**
	Easter Series™			
J.	1994 Mama & Baby Bunny™	18.95	**26**	**45**
K.	1994 Bunnies Book™	5.95	**10**	**20**
L.	1995 Grandpa Bunny & Herbie™	19.95	**21**	**40**

A. 1990 Father Christmas

8.5" Tall

Form No: 30066
No. Sold:

E. 1993 St. Nick

10.25" Tall

Form No: 31062
No. Sold:

• *Dresden Fun Facts* •

The Longaberger Museum was first opened in August 1990, but wasn't dedicated until November 1990 after "extensive improvements" were made. In 1996, the Museum underwent another major improvement being moved from its location on Main Street in Dresden to a special spot in the manufacturing building #1.

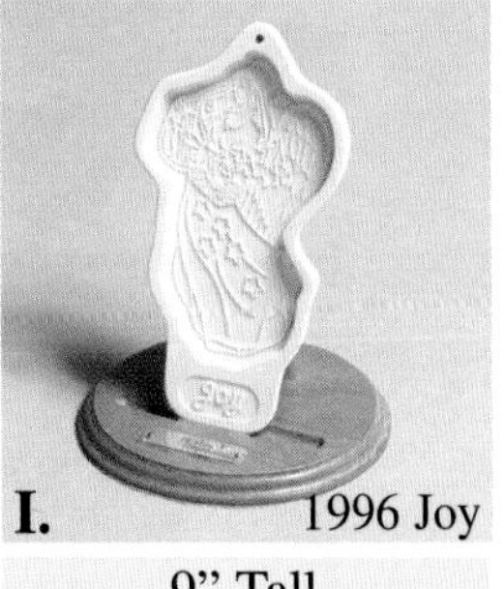

I. 1996 Joy

9" Tall

Form No: 31721
No. Sold:

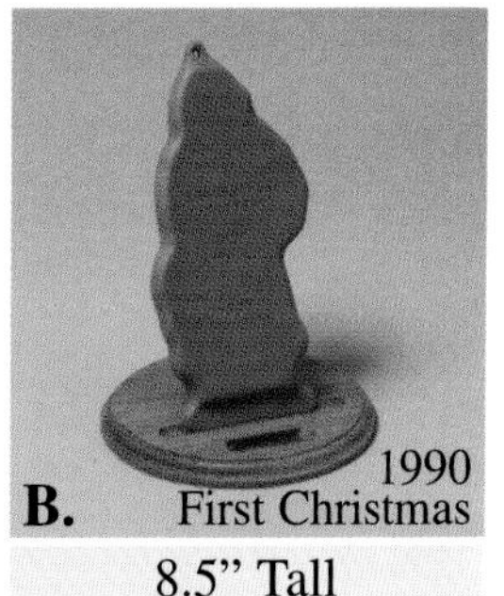
B. 1990 First Christmas

8.5" Tall

Form No: 30066
No. Sold: 3,200

Inscription reads: "Longaberger Pottery – First Casting– Christmas 1990"

C. 1991 Kriss Kringle

8.5" Tall

Form No: 30180
No. Sold:

D. 1992 Santa Claus

7.25" Tall

Form No: 30457
No. Sold:

F. 1993 Peace

7.5" Tall

Form No: 31071
No. Sold:

First year for this Series

G. 1994 Hope

9" Tall

Form No: 31356
No. Sold:

H. 1995 Love

7.5" Tall

Form No: 32468
No. Sold:

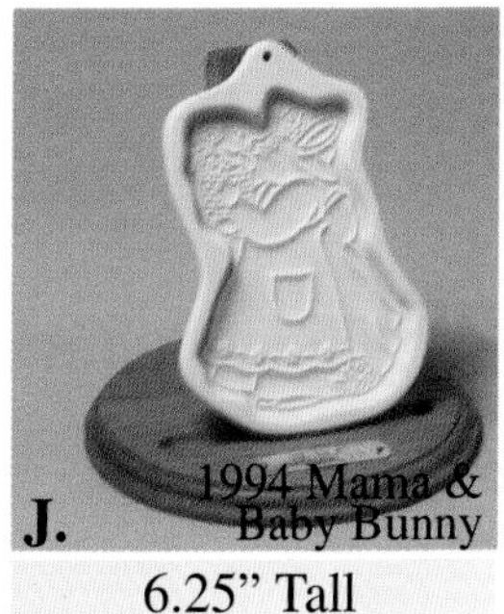
J. 1994 Mama & Baby Bunny

6.25" Tall

Form No: 31151
No. Sold:

K. 1994 Bunnies Book

Form No: 72079
No. Sold:

The 1994 Book was available only with a purchase. Only Hostesses were able to buy it for $5.95 and no additional purchase necessary.

L. 1995 Grandpa & Herbie

6.25L x 4.75H

Form No: 31500
No. Sold:

Features:

All Angel and Easter Series Cookie Molds are all made from Ivory Bisque Pottery.

Photo	Description		MARKET VALUES Original	Avg.	High
	Easter Series™ (con't)				
M.	1995	Bunnies™ Book	14.95	—	—
N.	1996	Rosemary Bunny™	19.95	**20**	**25**
O.	1997	Grandma Bunny & Lavender™	19.95	—	—
	Gingerbread Series:				
P.	1995	Country Cottage™	29.95	—	—
Q.	1996	Country Cabin™	29.95	—	—

M. 1995 Bunnies Book

Form No: 72796
No. Sold:

Last year that a book was offered.

N. 1996 Rosemary Bunny

6.5^{L} x 4.25^{H}

Form No: 32182
No. Sold:

O. 1997 Grandma & Lavender

4.5^{L} x 6.5^{W}

Form No: 32191
No. Sold:

P. 1995 Country Cottage

9^{L} x 13.25^{W}

Form No: 32476
No. Sold:

First year for this Series.

Q. 1996 Country Cabin

9^{L} x 13.25^{W}

Form No: 33090
No. Sold:

Bless Our Nest

Features:

Red and Blue Weave and Trim.
Burned in Crisco® Logo.
Series completed in 1993.

MARKET VALUES

Photo	Description		Original	Avg.	High
A.	1991	Pie™	79.95	**355**	**500**
		with Protector	89.90	**368**	**510**
B.	1992	Cookie™	29.95	**112**	**150**
		with **Protector**	35.90	**118**	**150**
		with **Liner**	40.90	**118**	**150**
		Combo **(P/L)**	39.95	**135**	**170**
C.	1992	Crisco Apron	13.95	**31**	**50**
D.	1993	Baking™	39.95	**81**	**110**
		with **Protector**	44.90	**94**	**110**
		with **Liner**	48.90	**94**	**110**
		Combo **(P/L)**	45.95	**110**	**150**
	Full Crisco® Collection Set			**636**	**800**

Crisco® is a registered trademark of The Procter & Gamble Company.

The Crisco® American™ Series started in 1991 when The Longaberger Company® was invited to create the official Pie Basket for the Crisco American Pie Celebration Bake-Off in New Orleans. Each of the 50 participants received the basket and then the company made it available to their customers to purchase. Although these baskets were sold during the All-American promotional season, they are not part of the All-American Series™. They were, however, designed to compliment that collection.

A. 1991 Pie

12^L x 12^W x 6^H

Form No: 100-DBRS
No. Sold:

Sold with a divider.

B. 1992 Cookie

10RD x 4^H

Form No: 10081
No. Sold:

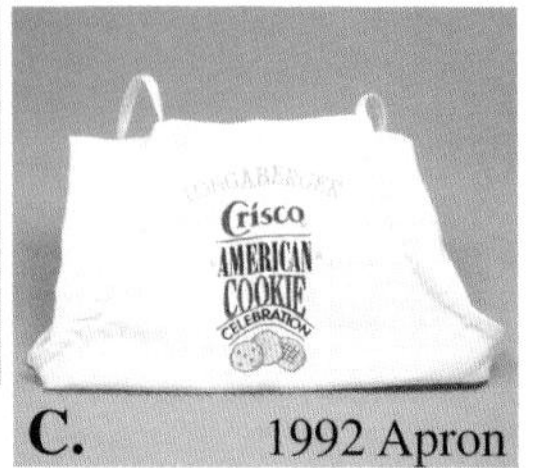

C. 1992 Apron

Not included in the Combo. Sold separately.

D. 1993 Baking

14.5^L x 7.5^W x 3.75^H

Form No: 104745
No. Sold:

Easter Series™

Features:

One stationary handle, except 1987 Medium Chore.

Photo		Description	MARKET VALUES Original	Avg.	High
	1987	Easter Signature Series			
A.		Medium Chore™	28.95	**91**	**115**
B.		Single Pie™	28.95	**97**	**115**
C.		Small Gathering™	28.95	**92**	**105**
D.		Spring™	25.95	**92**	**115**
E.	1988	Baby Easter™	18.95	**70**	**95**
F.		Small Easter™	22.95	**67**	**90**
G.		Medium Easter™	28.95	**76**	**95**
H.		Large Easter™	32.95	**80**	**95**
	1989	Stained Easter™[np]	29.95	**86**	**110**
I.		Blue Easter™	29.95	**84**	**105**
J.		Pink Easter™	29.95	**77**	**105**
K.	1990	Medium™	38.95	**74**	**100**
L.		Large™	43.95	**76**	**100**

Each of the *Easter Signature Baskets* from 1987 were delivered with Dave Longaberger's signature on it. In addition, only 100 total baskets have Grandma Bonnie's signature, as well.

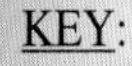
KEY: [np] = Not Pictured

A. 1987 Medium Chore

13^L x 8^W x 5^H

Form No: 3500-CX
No. Sold:

Easter Signature Series: Blue, red and green weave. Signed by Dave.

E. 1988 Baby Easter

7^L x 5^W x 3.5^H

Form No: 700-AN
No. Sold:

Available in natural only; blue, green, lilac, or pink weave.

I. 1989 Blue Easter

10RD x 4^H

Form No: 5500-ABS
No. Sold:

Available stained only; pink or blue weave, or no color.

B. 1987 Single Pie

12^L x 12^W x 4^H

Form No: 2200-AX
No. Sold:

Easter Signature Series: Blue, red and green weave. Signed by Dave.

C. 1987 Small Gathering

14^L x 9^W x 4.5^H

Form No: 2300-AX
No. Sold:

Easter Signature Series: Blue, red and green weave. Signed by Dave.

D. 1987 Spring

11^L x 8^W x 5.5^H

Form No: 900-AX
No. Sold:

Easter Signature Series: Blue, red and green weave. Signed by Dave.

F. 1988 Small Easter

10^L x 6^W x 4^H

Form No: 3400-AN
No. Sold:

Available in natural only; blue, green, lilac, or pink weave.

G. 1988

13^L x 8^W x 5^H

Form No: 3500-AN
No. Sold:

Available in natural only; blue, green, lilac, or pink weave.

H. 1988 Large Easter

14^L x 7.75^W x 5.25^H

Form No: 3600-AN
No. Sold:

Available in natural only; blue, green, lilac, or pink weave.

J. 1989 Pink Easter

10RD x 4^H

Form No: 5500-APS
No. Sold:

Available stained only; pink or blue weave, or no color.

K. 1990 Medium Easter

8RD x 4.5^H

Form No: 40000-APVBS
No. Sold:

Available stained only; Dresden blue, violet and pink weave.

L. 1990 Large Easter

9.5^{RD} x 5^H

Form No: 41000-APVBS
No. Sold:

Available stained only; Dresden blue, violet and pink weave.

Features:

One stationary handle,
except 1987 Medium Chore.

Photo		Description	Original	Avg.	High
M.	1991	Customer™	26.95	**59**	**95**
N.		Hostess™	21.95	**59**	**80**
O.	1992	Easter™	27.95	**66**	**85**
		with **P**rotector	32.90	**68**	**85**
		with **L**iner	40.90	**68**	**85**
		Combo **(P/L)**	39.95	**70**	**90**
P.	1993	Small Easter™	24.95	**59**	**75**
		with **P**rotector	28.90	**60**	**80**
		with **L**iner	34.90	**60**	**80**
		Combo **(P/L)**	35.95	**63**	**105**
Q.	1993	Large Easter™	27.95	**58**	**105**
		with **P**rotector	32.90	**60**	**105**
		with **L**iner	38.90	**60**	**105**
		Combo **(P/L)**	38.95	**67**	**110**
R.	1994	Easter™	49.95	**68**	**95**
		with **P**rotector	55.90	**68**	**95**
		with **L**iner	65.90	**68**	**95**
		Combo **(P/L)**	59.95	**70**	**100**
S.	1995	Easter™	49.95	**68**	**80**
		with **P**rotector	55.90	**70**	**85**
		with **L**iner	65.90	—	—
		Combo **(P/L)**	59.95	**83**	**90**
S.	1995	Happy Easter Tie-On	6.95	**9**	**12**
T.	1996	Easter™	39.95	**60**	**83**
		with **P**rotector	44.90	—	—
		with **L**iner	54.90	—	—
		Combo **(P/L)**	49.95	**63**	**100**
	1996	Easter Egg Tie-On	6.95	—	—
U.	1997	Small Easter™			
		Combo **(P/L)**	29.95	—	—
U	1997	Large Easter™	42.95	—	—
		with **P**rotector	48.90	—	—
		with **L**iner	57.90	—	—
		Combo **(P/L)**	52.95	—	—
U.	1997	Easter Egg Tie-On	6.95	—	—

M. 1991 Customer

$11^L \times 8^W \times 5.5^H$

Form No: 900-ATM*
No. Sold:

Available stained or natural; teal and mauve 3/8" weave.

Q. 1993 Large Easter

$10^L \times 6^W \times 4^H$

Form No: 13439
No. Sold:

Available stained or natural; teal shoestring weave.

U. 1997 Easter

Sm: $8.5^L \times 5^W \times 3.5^H$

Lg: $9.5^L \times 7^W \times 5^H$

Small: 63541
Large: 13447
Tie-On: 30007

Available stained or natural. Small only available as Combo and with a $42.95 purchase.

N. 1991 Hostess

7^L x 5^W x 3.5^H

Form No: 700-ATM•
No. Sold:

Available stained or natural; teal and mauve 3/8" weave.

O. 1992 Easter

10.5^L x 7.5^W x 4.5^H

Form No:34000-APVCNK
No. Sold:

Available stained or natural; Dresden blue, violet and pink weave.

P. 1993 Small Easter

7^L x 5^W x 3.5^H

Form No: 10774
No. Sold:

Available stained or natural; teal shoestring weave.

R. 1994 Easter

13.5^L x 8.25^W x 5.25^H

Form No: 16934
No. Sold:

Available stained, natural, stained with color or natural with color; Heartland® blue with pink accent weave.

S. 1995 Easter

10.75^L x 8.75^W x 5.25^H

Form No: 18708
Tie-On: 31518
No. Sold: 109,970

Available stained only; rose pink and purple weave. Tie-On sold separately.

T. 1996 Easter

5^L x 7.5^W x 6^H

Form No: 12912
Tie-On: 32271
No. Sold: 219,369

Available stained or natural; pink, green and purple double shoestring weave with purple and green.

• Basket Fun Facts •

Q Did the letters in the older form numbers stand for anything?

The letters in the older form numbers did stand for specific attributes of the baskets. They were set up to help customers visualize the baskets without seeing a picture or knowing its name. For example, when a customer saw the letter 'A' in a form number, they could tell that that basket had a stationary handle. The old form number system was set up as follows:

The first letter immediately after the number in each code was used to identify different features of the basket. The remaining letters were specific manufacturing codes pertaining to color or stain. The following are meanings for the letter that appear **immediately after the numeral:**

A	=	1 st/h	[Candle: 1100-**A**O]
B	=	1 sw/h	[Poinsettia: 3900-**B**RST]
C	=	2 sw/h	[Yuletide Traditions: 5100-**C**RST]
D	=	Lid	[Large Hamper: 1600-**D**O]
E	=	1 sw/h & Lid	[Tall Purse: 1000-**E**O]
F	=	2 sw/h & Lid	[Rectangular Sewing: 600-**F**]
G	=	1 st/h & Divider	[Cake: 100-**G**BRS]
H	=	2 sw/h, Divider & Lid or, 2 sw/h & Split Lid	[Large Picnic: 300 **H**BRS]
I	=	Loop on Back & Metal Hook	[Small Key: 700-**I**O]
J	=	Ears	[Darning: 500-**J**O]
K	=	Rockers & Ears	[Mini Cradle: 700- **K**O]
L	=	2 sw/h & Rockers	[Doll Cradle: 2500-**L**O]
M	=	Rockers	[Large Cradle: 2800-**M**]
N	=	1 sw/h, Lid & Stand	[Round Sewing: 3200-**N**O]
O	=	Plain basket	[Bread: 4700-**O**O]
P	=	Large Hanger	[Hanging 13": 4200-**P**O]
Q	=	1 st/h & Divided Lid	[Medium Purse: 900-**Q**O]
R	=	Legs	[Patio Planter: 6000-**R**]
S	=	13-inch Stand	[Small Fern Planter, 13": 2900-**S**O]
T	=	20-inch Stand	[Small Fern Planter, 20": 2900-**T**O]
U	=	1 sw/h (lengthwise) & Legs	[Magazine: 2100-**U**]
V&W	=	1 sw/h (lengthwise), Legs & Lid	[Magazine: 2100-**V**]
X&Y	=	Woven Lid & 2 Swinging Handles	[Weekender: 200-**Y**O]

Baskets with the same first numbers are made from the same form and have the same body dimensions. The differences can only be identified by the letters that follow. For example, Mini Cradle and the Small Key are both made with the same form (700); however, **KO** follows for the Mini Cradle while **IO** follows for the Small Key to distinguish their features.

Employee Baskets

Features:

Given to Employees for different occasions.
No original costs is associated with these baskets

Photo	Description	Avg.	High
	Birthday – Red shoestring weave and trim. Tags read "Longaberger Company Birthday Basket", Year of basket, and Employee's name (except 1990 did not have Employee's name).		
A.	1988 5" Measuring™	**77**	**105**
B.	1989 Sweetheart™	**76**	**95**
C.	1990 Potpourri™	**75**	**100**
D.	1991 Ivy™	**90**	**130**
E.	1992 Tour™	**62**	**85**
	Recognition – Given to Employees for years of service. Tag reads "Longaberger" or "Longaberger Company", the Year of award, and Achievement.		
	Sophomore[np] (1 yr.)	**67**	**75**
F.	Junior (2 yrs.)	**79**	**85**
	Senior[np] (5 yrs.)	**85**	**125**
G.	Senior Employee	**92**	**125**
H.	Master (10 yrs.)	**232**	**275**
	Perfect Attendance – Given out once a year to Employees who have maintained Perfect Attendance.		
I.	1994 Perfect Attendance	**420**	**425**
J.	1995 Perfect Attendance	**400**	**450**
K.	1996 Perfect Attendance	**—**	**—**

KEY: [np] = Not Pictured

A. 1988 5" Measuring

5RD x 4.5^{H}

Form No: 3800-
No. Sold:

E. 1992 Tour

8.75^{L} x 4.75^{W} x 6.5^{H}

Form No: 10022
No. Sold:

Last year for a Birthday Basket.

I. 1994 Perfect Attendance

6.5^{RD} x 5^{H}

Form No: unknown
No. Sold: ≈ 200

Lilac trim and shoestring weav around bottom. First Employe Basket to include accessories.

B. 1989 Sweetheart

5.75^{L} x 3.75^{W} x 3^{H}

Form No: 45000-
No. Sold:

C. 1990 Potpourri

5^{L} x 5^{W} x 2.5^{H}

Form No: 13000-
No. Sold:

Tag did not include Employee's name in this year.

D. 1991 Ivy

5.5^{L} x 5.5^{W} x 2.5^{H}

Form No: 13100-
No. Sold:

F. Junior Recognition

8.75^{L} x 4.75^{W} x 6.5^{H}

Form No: unknown
No. Sold:

Sophomore — same, except no color weaving. Senior — same, except with blue trim and weave.

G. Senior Employee

16^{L} x 9^{W} x 6^{H}

Form No: unknown
No. Sold:

H. Master Employee

12.5^{RD} x 13.5^{H}

Form No: 1900-
No. Sold:

Given to Employees with 10 years of service with the company.

J. 1995 Perfect Attendance

7RD x 4.5^{H}

Form No: unknown
No. Sold:

K. 1996 Perfect Attendance

9^{L} x 5^{W} x 5^{H}

Form No: unknown
No. Sold: ≈ 309

Features:

Given to Employees for Different Occasions.
No Original Cost is associated with these baskets.

Photo	Description		MARKET VALUES Avg.	High
	Christmas – Red and green alternating shoestring weave. No color on trim. Tags read "Merry Christmas", Year, and "Longaberger Company".			
L.	1987	Medium Market™	**235**	**310**
M.	1988	Cake™	**143**	**180**
N.	1989	Candle™	**125**	**150**
O.	1990	Small Gathering™	**110**	**140**
P.	1991	Tall Key™	**108**	**120**
Q.	1992	5" Measuring™	**94**	**120**
R.	1993	Button™	**90**	**110**
S.	1994	Tea™	**93**	**120**
T.	1995	Ambrosia™	**87**	**95**
U.	1996	Cracker™	—	—

L. 1987 Medium Market

$15^{L} \times 10^{W} \times 7.5^{H}$

Form No: 500-
No. Sold:

P. 1991 Tall Key

$9.5^{L} \times 5^{W} \times 9.5^{H}$

Form No: 1000-
No. Sold:

T. 1995 Ambrosia

$5.5^{L} \times 4^{W} \times 4^{H}$

Form No: 10120
No. Sold:

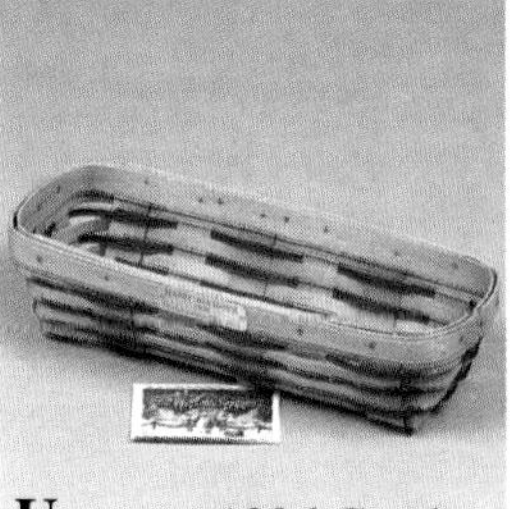

U. 1996 Cracker

$11.5^{L} \times 5^{W} \times 3^{H}$

Form No: 4500-
No. Sold:

M. 1988 Cake

12^{L} x 12^{W} x 6^{H}

Form No: 100-
No. Sold:

N. 1989 Candle

9^{L} x 5^{W} x 5^{H}

Form No: 1100-
No. Sold:

O. 1990 Small Gathering

14^{L} x 9^{W} x 4.5^{H}

Form No: 2300-
No. Sold:

Q. 1992 5" Measuring

5RD x 4.5^{H}

Form No: 3800-
No. Sold:

R. 1993 Button

7RD x 3^{H}

Form No: 5400-
No. Sold:

S. 1994 Tea

7^{L} x 5^{W} x 3.5^{H}

Form No: 700-
No. Sold:

• *Basket Fun Facts* •

Now you can see what it is like to be a Longaberger® weaver on your next Dresden tour.

MADE ON TOUR AT
LONGABERGER®
DRESDEN, OHIO USA

LONGABERGER®
MAKE A BASKET SHOP™

The Longaberger® Make a Basket Shop™ is located on Main Street in Dresden in the same building where the Museum used to be located, across from Popeye's. The cost is only $54.95 (plus tax), but you must be 12 years or older to participate. Currently, the Make A Basket™ is the Spring form, but is expected to change on a regular basis so collectors will be able to collect their very own Make A Basket Collection™. The logos shown are burned into the bottom of each one for authenticity.

• Basket Fun Facts •

Identifying J.W. Originals

J.W. Longaberger was the inspiration behind The Longaberger Company® (see page 2 for more information about this history). He wove baskets with his dad in the early 1900's to help provide for his family.

Baskets that were woven by J.W. himself are referred to as "J.W. Originals". They do not have any identifying marks, such as signatures or stamps. While some collectors claim to be able to spot a J.W. Original easily, the only experts in this area are the members of the Longaberger family. If you come across a basket that you think is a J.W. Original, we encourage you to either have the owner have it authenticated by a family member, or you investigate its authenticity before purchasing.

Although there are no obvious identifying marks, J.W. did have some "trade-mark" workmanship. The following are tips that family members have published as a few things to look for in a J.W. Original:

- J.W. always made a very tight basket, sometimes leaving it on the form overnight.
- Corners are more square than rounded due to tightness.
- Baskets with stationary handles were tacked with three tacks in the shape of an upside down ' V ' design.
- Many of his baskets were made with hand-carved handles. If the handle is very smooth, it was probably hand-carved.
- All of the baskets in the J.W. Collection® were made from an original J.W. design. While these may have been his most common forms used, there are others that he made.

Look for more information about J.W. Originals in future Bentley Guides®.

Father's Day™

Features:

Dresden Blue and Burgundy Trim and Weave.

MARKET VALUES

Photo	Description		Original	Avg.	High
A.	1991	Spare Change™	21.95	**109**	**140**
		with **Protector**	25.90	**109**	**145**
		with **Liner**	32.90	**109**	**145**
		with Combo **(P/L)**	32.95	**115**	**150**
B.	1992	Paper™	23.95	**105**	**130**
		with **Protector**	27.90	**105**	**135**
		with **Liner**	33.90	**115**	**135**
		Combo **(P/L)**	33.95	**115**	**150**
C.	1992	Pencil™	20.95	**110**	**135**
		with **Protector**	23.90	**110**	**140**
		with **Liner**	30.90	**110**	**140**
		Combo **(P/L)**	29.95	**127**	**175**
D.	1994	Tissue™	29.95	**86**	**105**
		with **Protector**	35.90	**86**	**105**
		with **Lid**	42.90	**90**	**105**
		Combo **(P/Lid)**	39.95	**90**	**110**
E.	1994	Business Card™	22.95	**85**	**140**
		Combo **(P)**	25.90	**90**	**155**
		with **Liner** (1995)	31.90	**90**	**155**
		Full Set **(Combo/L)**	34.85	**90**	**165**
F.	1995	Mini Waste™	46.95	**78**	**120**
		Combo **(P)**	49.95	**82**	**135**
		with **Liner**	63.95	**78**	**120**
		with **Lid**	63.95	**78**	**100**
		Full Set **(P/L/Lid)**	83.85	**92**	**135**
G.	1996	Address™	29.95	—	—
		with **Protector**	33.90	—	—
		Combo **(P/Card Holder)**	34.95	**63**	**90**
		with **Liner**	42.90	—	—
		with **Lid**	43.90	—	—
		Full Set **(Combo/L/Lid)**	61.85	**72**	**100**
H.	1997	Personal Organizer™	39.95	—	—
		with **Protector**	46.90	—	—
		with **Liner**	57.90	—	—
		Combo **(P/L)**	54.95	—	—
		with **Lid**	62.90	—	—
		Full Set **(Combo/Lid)**	77.90	—	—

A. 1991 Spare Change

6.5^L x 6.5^W x 3^H

Form No: 1300-JCWS
No. Sold:

Liner also available in new design starting 1995.

E. 1994 Business Card

4.75^L x 3.75^W x 2.25^H

Form No: 17477
No. Sold:

Hostess only. Liner was not originally offered – available for the first time in 1995, in new fabric design only.

B. 1992 Paper

7.5^{L} x 5.5^{W} x 2^{FH} x 3.5^{BH}

Form No: 16000
No. Sold:

Included note paper. Liner also available in new design starting

C. 1992 Pencil

4RD x 4.25^{H}

Form No: 15000
No. Sold:

Liner also available in new design starting 1995.

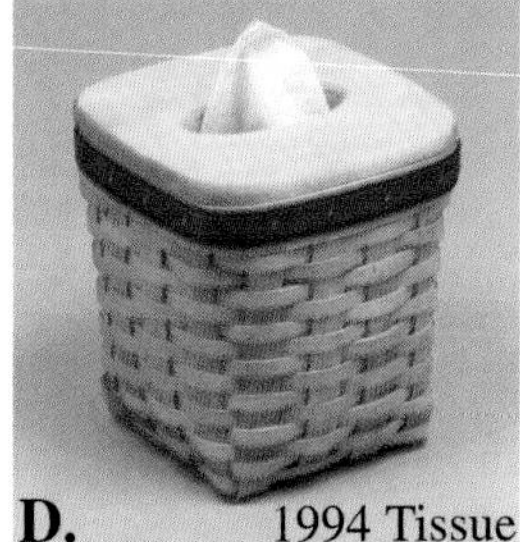

D. 1994 Tissue

6.5^{L} x 6.5^{W} x 6.25^{H}

Form No: 18490
No. Sold:

No Liner available.

F. 1995 Mini Waste

7.5^{L} x 7.5^{W} x 10^{H}

Form No: 11266
No. Sold:

Lid and Liner sold separately. First year for the newly designed fabric.

G. 1996 Address Basket

8.25^{L} x 6.25^{W} x 3.75^{H}

Form No: 12611
No. Sold:

Combo included Protector, Address Cards and Card Holder. Lid and Liner sold separately.

H. 1997 Personal Organizer

14^{L} x 6^{W} x 3^{H}

Form No: 63134
No. Sold:

Combo came with divided protector. Regular protector was also available for $5.95.

• *Dresden Fun Facts* •

Dresden has not always been know as Dresden. It's original name was "Wakatomika", which is Shawnee for "Eastern Town".

Over 400,000 people visited Dresden in 1996 with a projected 500,000 + for 1997.

• Baskets Fun Facts •

The Longaberger Company® is a success story that has one main theme: setting goals and then *over achieving* them. Throughout the history of the company, projections that have been set have been attained well before the projection dates.

For example, in 1983, The Company offered a Hamper promotion and projected 8,000 to be sold. Over 20,000 were sold. A couple of months later they offered a promotion on the Magazine basket and instead of selling the projected 24,000 baskets, they sold 44,000.

This example is not an isolated case. The 1996 Easter Basket set records as the most successful selling campaign for the company selling 219,369 baskets. That is until the very next campaign, 1996 Mother's Day broke this new record with 224,278 baskets!

$500 Million Basket
[see page 83]

Recently, The Longaberger Company® celebrated yet another benchmark: $500 Million in sales. This achievement was attained in November of 1996. The entire year topped $520 Million.

Here are some projections The Company has put forth for the future. Let's watch and see if their record breaking streaks continue:

1997 estimated sales: $650 Million
1998 estimated sales: $850 Million
2000 estimated sales: $1 Billion (this is doubling sales in just 4 years)

In 1996, the company welcomed 12,300 new Consultants, bringing the sales force to nearly 35,000. They also promoted 351 consultants to Branch Advisor, 35 to Regional Advisor and 2 to Director.

1997 estimated number of Directors: 30
2000 estimated number of Directors: 76
2000 estimated total Consultants: 70,000 (this is doubling growth in 3 years)

Feature Baskets

FEATURE BASKETS

Features:

Baskets featured for a limited time.
This section is divided in two sections:
with and without color weaving.

Photo	Description	Original	Avg.	High
	Baskets featured WITH Color Weaving:			
A.	1987 Resolution™	16.95	**117**	**150**
B.	1988 Memory™		**132**	**165**
	& 89 with Longaberger Book	39.95	**162**	**180**
C.	1990 Basket O'Luck™	36.95	**110**	**140**
D.	1990 Heartland Getaway™	65.95	**140**	**160**
E.	1990 Shamrock™	19.95	**118**	**150**
F.	1993 All-Star Trio™	29.95	**62**	**110**
G.	1993 Thank-You Basket™	N/A	**126**	**150**
H.	1994 Boo™	34.95	**84**	**115**
	with **P**rotector	39.90	**86**	**115**
	with **L**iner	48.90	**86**	**115**
	Combo **(P/L)**	44.95	**90**	**130**
I.	1994 Woven Traditions Pie™	37.95	**64**	**85**
	with **P**rotector	45.90	**67**	**85**
	with **L**iner	55.90	**67**	**85**
	Combo **(P/L/Plate)**	79.95	**80**	**95**
J.	1994 Three Key Baskets	98.95	**123**	**135**
	Small Key™	27.95	**37**	**50**
	Medium Key™	29.95	**43**	**50**
	Tall Key™	40.95	**48**	**60**
K.	1995 Pumpkin Basket™	47.95	**76**	**120**
	with **P**rotector	54.90	**90**	**120**
	with **L**iner	64.90	**90**	**120**
	Combo **(P/L)**	59.95	**95**	**125**
	with **Lid**	72.90	**95**	**125**
	Full Set **(Combo/Lid)**	84.90	**123**	**160**
K.	1995 Pumpkin™ Tie-On	6.95	**13**	**17**
L.	1996 Small Pumpkin™	40.95	**65**	**85**
	with **P**rotector	45.90	—	—
	with **L**iner	55.90	—	—
	with Combo **(P/L)**	52.95	**73**	**90**
	with **Lid**	60.90	—	—
	Full Set **(Combo/Lid)**	72.90	**85**	**105**

A. 1987 Resolution

$5^{RD} \times 4.5^{H}$

Form No: 3800-ABS
No. Sold:

Offered in the month of December 1987

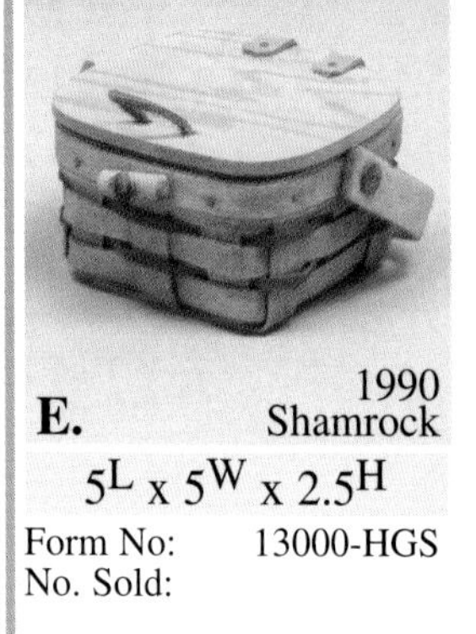

E. 1990 Shamrock

$5^{L} \times 5^{W} \times 2.5^{H}$

Form No: 13000-HGS
No. Sold:

I. 1994 Woven Traditions Pie

$12^{L} \times 12^{W} \times 4^{H}$

Form No: 12211
No. Sold:

Combo included Liner, Protector and Pie Plate.

B. 1988 & 89 Memory

8.75^{L} x 4.75^{W} x 6.5^{H}

Form No: 5600-BBS
No. Sold:

Only sold as a combo of book and basket.

C. 1990 Basket O'Luck

5.5^{RD} x 3.75^{H}

Form No: 17000-AGS
No. Sold:

Hostess only

D. 1990 Heartland Getaway

17^{L} x 14^{W} x 11^{H}

Form No: 300-CCS
No. Sold:

Hostess only

F. 1993 All-Star Trio

5.75^{L} x 3.75^{W} x 3^{H}

Form No: 64408
No. Sold:

Sold only as a three-piece combo.

G. 1993 Thank-You

11^{L} x 8^{W} x 5.5^{H}

Form No: 190xx
No. Sold: 7,478

This basket was sent as a Thank-You from Dave to the customers who had ordered the Red Pottery and waited for it through its production problems.

H. 1994 Boo

11^{L} x 8^{W} x 5.5^{H}

Form No: 10987
No. Sold:

J. 1994 Key Basket Set

Form No:
Sm: **R**17078 /**B** -51 /**G** -60
Md: **R**15172 /**B** -99/**G** -81
Tall: **R**14672 /**B** -99 /**G** -81

Available in Red, Blue, or Green weave.

K. 1995 Pumpkin

9.25^{RD} x 7.25^{H}

Form No: 19402
Tie-On: 31763
No. Sold:

L. 1996 Small Pumpkin

7.25^{RD} x 5.25^{H}

Form No: 16012
No. Sold

Features:

Baskets featured for a limited time.
This section is divided in two sections:
with and without color weaving.

Photo		Description	Original	Avg.	High
		1996 Six Baskets / Three Colors Promotion			
M.	1996	Medium Berry™	29.95	—	—
		with **P**rotector	33.90	—	—
		with **L**iner	42.90	—	—
		Combo **(P/L)**	36.43	—	—
	1996	Medium Spoon™[np]	36.95	—	—
		with **P**rotector	42.90	—	—
		with **L**iner	52.90	—	—
		Combo **(P/L)**	44.93	—	—
	1996	Pantry™[np]	46.95	—	—
		with **P**rotector	56.90	—	—
		with **L**iner	64.90	—	—
		Combo **(P/L)**	55.93	—	—
	1996	Large Vegetable™[np]	61.95	—	—
		with **P**rotector	71.90	—	—
		with **L**iner	82.90	—	—
		Combo **(P/L)**	72.43	—	—
N.	1996	Large Market™	77.95	—	—
		with **P**rotector	90.90	—	—
		with **L**iner	106.90	—	—
		Combo **(P/L)**	92.43	—	—
O.	1996	Remembrance™	99.95	—	—
		with **P**rotector	110.90	—	—
		with **L**iner	125.90	—	—
		Combo **(P/L)**	112.93	—	—
		Baskets featured WITHOUT Color Weaving:			
A.	1981	Grandma Bonnie's Bread & Milk™		**675**	**750**
B.	1982	Oak Lid Picnic ™		**467**	**600**
C.	1984	Patio Planter™	21.95	**88**	**105**
D.	1984	Shaker Peg Basket™	14.95	**45**	**60**
	1985	Single Pie™[WL]	19.95	—	—
E.	1985	Pantry™	21.95	**55**	**70**
F.	1985 & 87	Two-Quart™	28.95	**74**	**80**
G.	1985 & 87	Round Sewing™ (no stand)	37.95	**160**	**190**

KEY

[np] = Not Pictured

[WL] = *Wish List*™. It is similar to what is available today. Pictures can be found in a current *Wish List*™. See the *Quick Find* for dimensions and form numbers.

M. 1996 Med.Berry

7.5^L x 7.5^W x 3.5^H

Form No: 16241/25/33
No. Sold:

Liner was only available in stand-up.

A. 1981 Bread & Milk

16^L x 8^W x 11^H

Form No: 2100-
No. Sold:

First Tagged Basket

E. 1985 Pantry

14^L x 9^W x 4.5^H

Form No: 2300-JO
No. Sold:

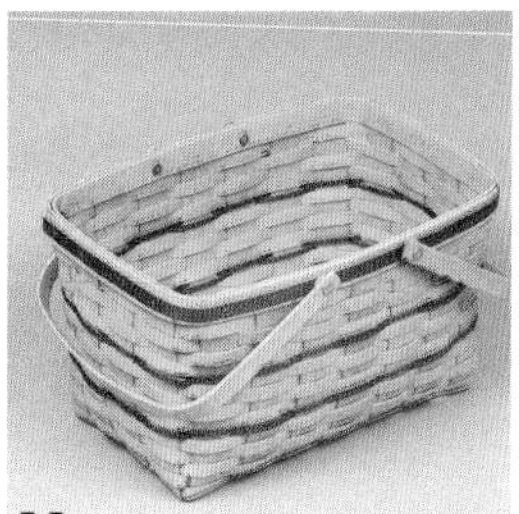

N. 1996 Lg.Market

16^{L} x 11^{W} x 9^{H}

Form No: 16641/24/32
No. Sold:

Liner was only available in over-the-edge.

O. 1996 Remembrance

10.5^{L} x 9^{W} x 8^{H}

Form No: 16648/21/30
No. Sold:

Hostess Only.
Liner was only available in over-the-edge.

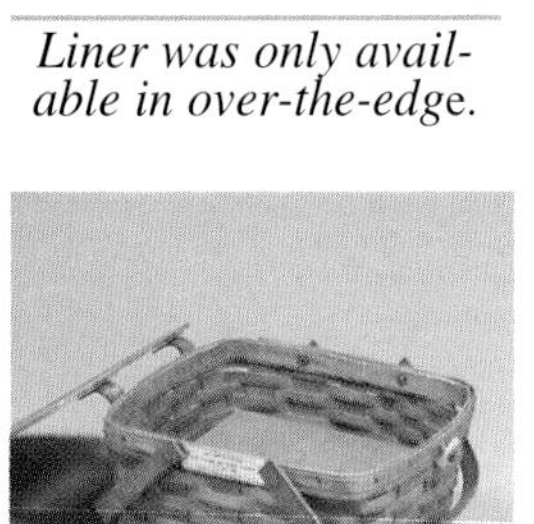

B. 1982 Oak Lid Picnic

12^{L} x 12^{W} x 6^{H}

Form No: unknown
No. Sold: < 2,500

2,500 were to be made, but far less were actually produced.

C. 1984 Patio Planter

10RD x 5.5^{H}

Form No: 6000-R
No. Sold:

D. 1984 Shaker Peg

5.5^{L} x 5.5^{W} x 6^{H}

Form No: 10000-AO
No. Sold:

F. 1985,1987 Two-Quart

9.5^{L} x 5^{W} x 9.5^{H}

Form No: 1000-CO
No. Sold:

G. 1985, 1987 Round Sewing

13RD x 8.5^{H}

Form No: 3200-EO
No. Sold:

Features:

Baskets are listed in chronological order, by the year they were featured.

Photo	Description		Original	Avg.	High
			MARKET VALUES		
	1985	Berry Baskets™ (1 st/h)			
H.	& 88	Small	16.95	**33**	**45**
I.		Medium	17.95	**35**	**45**
J.		Large	18.95	**40**	**60**
	1986	Chore Baskets™ (2 sw/h)			
		Small [np]	17.95	**55**	**60**
K.		Medium	18.95	**53**	**55**
		Large[np]	23.95	**51**	**60**
	1986	Daisy™, Natural[np]	27.95	**63**	**70**
L.	1986 & 87	Daisy™, Stained	25.95	**68**	**95**
M.	1986	Large Hamper™	79.95	**208**	**280**
N.	1986	Herb™		**72**	**95**
O.		Garden™		**83**	**110**
		Sold only as a Set	32.90	—	—
P.	1987	Bakery™	22.95	**42**	**50**
Q.	1987	Lg.Inverted Waste™	59.95	**124**	**150**
	1987	Med.Market™[WL]	41.95	—	—
	1987	Med.Gathering™[WL]	41.95	—	—
	(Hostess Only. Both offered only Natural or Natural with color.)				
R.	1987 & 88	Weekender™	54.95	**155**	**170**

KEY

[np] = Not Pictured

[WL] = *Wish List*™. It is similar to what is available today. Pictures can be found in a current *Wish List*™. See the *Quick Find* for dimensions and form numbers.

H. 1985, 1988 Small Berry

$6.5^L \times 6.5^W \times 3^H$

Form No: 1300-AO
No. Sold:

L. 1986, 87 Daisy, Stained

$10^{RD} \times 4^H$

Form No: 5500-AO
No. Sold:

In '86, this basket was available in both Natural and Stained. In '87, it was only offered Stained.

P. 1987 Bakery

$14.5^L \times 7.5^W \times 3.75^H$

Form No: 4700-JO
No. Sold:

I. 1985, 1988 Medium Berry

7.5^{L} x 7.5^{W} x 3.5^{H}

Form No: 1400-AO
No. Sold:

J. 1985, 1988 Large Berry

8.5^{L} x 8.5^{W} x 5^{H}

Form No: 1500-AO
No. Sold:

These 1985 and 1988 features were the only times that the Berry Baskets™ were offered with 1 stationary handle.

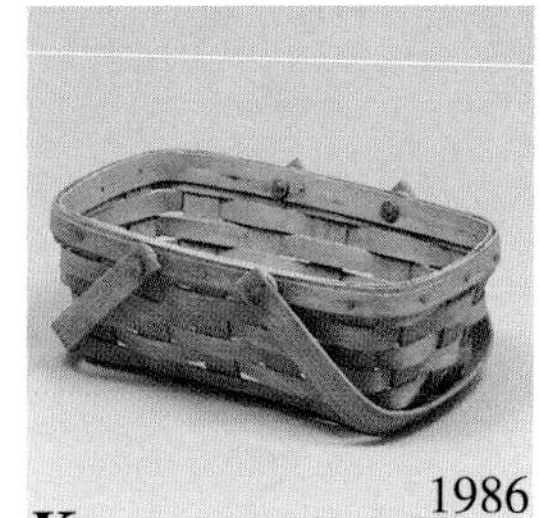

K. 1986 Medium Chore

13^{L} x 8^{W} x 5^{H}

Form No: 3500-CO
No. Sold:

Small: 10^{L} x 6^{W} x 4^{H}
Large: 14^{L} x 7.75^{W} x 5.25^{H}

M. 1986 Large Hamper

16.5^{L} x 16.5^{W} x 21.5^{H}

Form No: 1600-OO
No. Sold:

This was a May feature where only Hostesses could purchase it half priced. No lid. First time for hand slots.

N. 1986 Herb

11.5^{L} x 5^{W} x 3^{H}

Form No: 4500-AO
No. Sold:

O. 1986 Garden

15^{L} x 8^{W} x 2.25^{H}

Form No: 4600-AO
No. Sold:

Q. 1987 Large Inverted Waste

14RD x 16^{H}

Form No: 2000-BO
No. Sold:

R. 1987, 88 Weekender

10.5^{L} x 9^{W} x 8^{H}

Form No: 200-YO
No. Sold:

FEATURE BASKETS

Features:
Blue Accent Weave and Trim.
Commemorative Brass Tag.
Series Retired in 1994.

Photo	Description		MARKET VALUES Original	Avg.	High
	1988	Planters (with legs)			
S.		Small Fern™	35.95	**125**	**140**
T.		Large Fern™	42.95	**140**	**140**
U.	1989	Bed™	18.95	**85**	**90**
		with **L**iner	29.95	**89**	**110**
V.	1989	Breakfast™	24.95	**80**	**105**
		with **L**iner	37.95	**87**	**110**
		Bed / Breakfast Set	43.90	**140**	**150**
		with **L**iner	67.90	**152**	**160**
W.	1989	Friendship™	21.95	**55**	**75**
	Shades of Autumn Hostesses				
X.	1991	Small Hamper™	99.95	**153**	**160**
		with **P**rotector	113.90	—	—
X.	1991	Large Hamper™	149.95	**220**	**250**
		with **P**rotector	169.90	—	—
	1993	Large Hamper[WL]	179.95	**230**	**250**
	&94	Combo **(P)**	185.95	**243**	**280**
Y.	1994	Hostess Appreciation	N/C	**74**	**120**
Z.	1995	Horizon of Hope™	28.95	**58**	**80**
		with **P**rotector	31.90	**58**	**80**
		with **L**iner	38.90	**58**	**80**
		Combo **(P/L)**	41.85	**65**	**90**
A[1]	1996	Hostess Appreciation	N/C	**72**	**85**
B[1]	1996	Horizon of Hope™	28.95	—	—
		with **P**rotector	31.90	—	—
		with **L**iner	38.90	—	—
		Combo **(P/L)**	41.85	**57**	**65**

KEY

[WL] = *Wish List*™. It is similar to what is available today. Pictures can be found in a current *Wish List*™. See the *Quick Find* for dimensions and form numbers.

S. 1988 Small Planter

8.5RD x 7.5^{H}

Form No: 2900-RO
No. Sold:

W. 1989 Friendship

5.5^{L} x 5.5^{W} x 2.5^{H}

Form No: 13100-JO
No. Sold:

Made using 1/2" weave.

A[1] 1996 Hostess Appreciation

5.5^{L} x 5.5^{W} x 2.5^{H}

Form No: unknown
No. Sold: 181,337

Given to Hostesses with shows in both Oct. 95 and Jan. 96. Liner was sold separately.

T. 1988 Large Planter

13RD x 8.5^{H}

Form No: 3200-RO
No. Sold:

U. 1989 Bed

11.5^{L} x 5^{W} x 3^{H}

Form No: 4500-AO
No. Sold:

V. 1989 Breakfast

14.5^{L} x 7.5^{W} x 3.75^{H}

Form No: 4700-AO
No. Sold:

X. 1991 Shades of Autumn

12^{L} x 12.25^{W} x 16.25^{H}

Sm.Hamper: 1700-DS
Lg.Hamper: 1600-DS

Large: 16.5^{L} x 16.5^{W} x 21.5^{H} Only available to Hostesses during the Shades of Autumn campaign in 1991. Both hampers have detached lids, knob in center of lid and two hand slots.

Y. 1994 Hostess Appreciation

8^{L} x 4^{W} x 2^{H}

Form No: unknown
No. Sold:

Given to Hostesses with shows in both Oct. 93 and Jan. 94.

Z. 1995 Horizon of Hope

5.75^{L} x 3.75^{W} x 3^{H}

Form No: 17124
No. Sold: 180,579

All Regular line fabrics were made available for this Liner.

B1 1996 Horizon of Hope

6.75^{L} x 4.75^{W} x 2.25^{H}

Form No: 15911
No. Sold: 225,663

Each basket came with a set of 12 recipes chosen by The American Cancer Society®.

About the Horizon of Hope™ . . .

With the 1996 campaign, The Longaberger Company, along with its Consultants and Collectors, was able to raise $597,906 for the American Cancer Society®. This brings their total contribution over the two years to $1,061,128. Thrilled with their customers commitment to finding a cure for Breast Cancer, The Company has committed to the American Cancer Society to offer the Horizon of Hope campaign for five years, taking it through the year 1999.

• Basket Fun Facts •

In *The Longaberger Story*, Dave Longaberger lists his eighteen management principles that have been the foundation to his success. Here are what he considers to be the "Top 10"

Longaberger Top 10 Management Principles

#10 Look at old pictures - reminds you of why you think and act the way that you do.

#9 Intelligence is only understanding

#8 Know your labor and material costs

#7 Market yourself

#6 People are first

#5 Know what you want to do

#4 Have patience

#3 Trust People

#2 Listen to People

and the #1 Top 10 Management Principle is:

Know yourself

This information is from *The Longaberger Story - And How We Did It.*
This book can be purchased in select Dresden stores.

Holiday Hostess™

Features:

Red and Green Weave.
Red or Green Trim.

Photo	Description		Original	Avg.	High
			MARKET VALUES		
A.	1987	Tray™	32.95	**109**	**185**
B.	1988	Tall Key™	30.95	**92**	**125**
C.	1988	Weekender™	65.95	**183**	**225**
D.	1988	Large Market™	49.95	**114**	**140**
E.	1988	Small Laundry™	67.95	**270**	**350**
F.	1989	Medium Gathering™	40.95	**104**	**135**
G.	1989	Large Fruit™	49.95	**133**	**165**
H.	1989	Magazine™	53.95	**117**	**160**
I.	1990	13" Measuring™	69.95	**123**	**155**
J.	1990	Large Gathering™	65.95	**124**	**160**
K.	1991	Tree Trimming™	79.95	**163**	**275**
		Combo (**P**)	92.90	**165**	**300**
L.	1992	Gift Giving™	124.95	**158**	**200**
		with **P**rotector	137.90	**158**	**225**
		with **L**iner	146.90	**158**	**225**
		Combo (**P/L**)	169.85	**158**	**250**

A. 1987 Tray

14^L x 9^W x 4.5^H

Form No: 2300-JGRS
No. Sold:

E. 1988 Small Laundry

24^L x 17^W x 10^H

Form No: 2600-ORGS
No. Sold:

About the Holiday Hostess . . .

Holiday Hostess baskets are only available to hostesses during the Holiday selling season. This season usually begins Sept. 1 and goes through the end of the year. It is very common for the original collector to have purchased these baskets at half price, using their hostess benefits.

I. 1990 13" Measuring

13RD x 12.5^H

Form No: 4200-CGRS
No. Sold:

KEY

† = Form Numbers are listed as **Red** weave / **Green** weave

B. 1988 Tall Key

9.5^{L} x 5^{W} x 9.5^{H}

Form No: 1000-IRGS
No. Sold:

C. 1988 Weekender

10.5^{L} x 9^{W} x 8^{H}

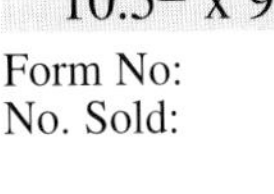

Form No: 200-YRGS
No. Sold:

D. 1988 Large Market

16^{L} x 11^{W} x 9^{H}

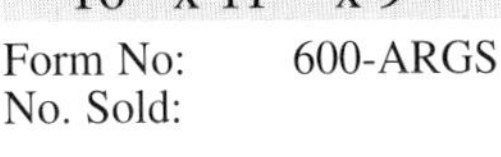

Form No: 600-ARGS
No. Sold:

F. 1989 Medium Gathering

18^{L} x 11^{W} x 4.5^{H}

Form No: 2400-AGRS
No. Sold:

G. 1989 Large Fruit

13RD x 8.5^{H}

Form No: 3200-BGRS
No. Sold:

H. 1989 Magazine

16^{L} x 8^{W} x 11^{H}

Form No: 2100-CGRS
No. Sold:

J. 1990 Large Gathering

19^{L} x 12^{W} x 6^{H}

Form No: 2500-CGRS
No. Sold:

K. 1991 Tree Trimming

12.5^{RD} x 13.5^{H}

Form No: 1900-BRGS
No. Sold:

L. 1992 Gift Giving

20.5^{L} x 15^{W} x 10.5^{H}

Form No: 12700/12718†
No. Sold:

Features:

Available only to Hostesses.

Photo		Description	Original	Avg.	High
M.	1993	Homecoming™	109.95	**169**	**250**
		with **P**rotector	120.90	**169**	**250**
		with **L**iner	131.90	**169**	**250**
		with **Lid**	145.90	**169**	**250**
		Combo **(P/L/Lid)**	149.95	**172**	**265**
N.	1994	Sleigh Bell™	139.95	**182**	**250**
		with **P**rotector	154.90	—	—
		with **L**iner	167.90	—	—
		with **Lid**	175.90	—	—
		Combo **(P/L/Lid)**	199.95	**185**	**250**
O.	1995	Evergreen™	139.95	**180**	**225**
		with **P**rotector	154.90	—	—
		with **L**iner	167.90	—	—
		with **Lid**	179.90	—	—
		Combo **(P/L/Lid)**	199.95	**185**	**250**
		with Divider	146.90	—	—
P.	1996	Yuletide Treasures™	129.95	—	—
		with **P**rotector	144.90	—	—
		with **L**iner	159.90	—	—
		with **Lid**	179.90	—	—
		Combo **(P/L/Lid)**	199.95	—	—

(Avg. and High are MARKET VALUES.)

M. 1993 Homecoming

15^L x 15^W x 7.5^H

Form No: 12084/12092†
No. Sold:

N. 1994 Sleigh Bell

16.5^{RD} x 11.5^H

Form No: 14427/14435†
No. Sold:

Lid available with red or green knob.

KEY

† = Form Numbers are listed as:

Red weave / **Green** weave

O. 1995 Evergreen

15.5^L x 15.5^W x 12.25^H

Form No: 19607/19615†
No. Sold:

Lid available with red or green knob. Divider shelf sold separately.

P. 1996 Yuletide Treasures

13.75^L x 20.25^W x 7.5^H

Form No: 18619/18627†
No. Sold:

The lid that was introduced for this basket is still available in the regular line.

Hostess Collection™

Features:

Available only to Hostesses. Baskets from 1990 to present have 3/8" weave.

Photo	Description	Original	Avg.	High
	1986 – 1990:			
A.	Large Hamper™	109.95	**220**	**275**
	Medium Hamper ™[np]	69.95	**135**	**165**
B.	Doll Cradle™	44.95	**162**	**225**
C.	Large (Infant) Cradle™	109.95	**300**	**400**
D.	Large Laundry™	96.95	**183**	**275**
	1990 – 1992:			
E.	Heirloom™	87.95	**133**	**180**
F.	Hearthside ™	59.95	**96**	**115**
	with Protector	68.90	**105**	**140**
G.	Remembrance™	79.95	**150**	**200**
	with Protector	88.90	**169**	**240**
H.	Harvest™	54.95	**89**	**105**
	with Protector	66.90	**90**	**105**
	1992 – 1995:			
I.	Gourmet Picnic™	99.95	**130**	**170**
	with **P**rotector	110.90	**130**	**170**
	with **L**iner	121.90	**130**	**170**
	Combo **(P/L)**	132.85	**140**	**175**
	1992 – 1996:			
J.	Mail™	79.95	**118**	**130**
	with **P**rotector	89.90	**121**	**130**
	with **L**iner	96.90	**121**	**130**
	Combo **(P/L)**	106.85	**126**	**160**

[please note: The 1991 Shades of Autumn Hostess Hampers have been moved to the *Feature Section*]

KEY: [np] = Not Pictured

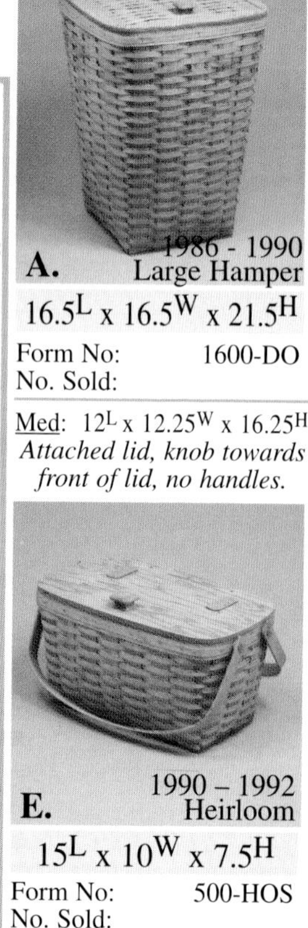

A. 1986 - 1990 Large Hamper

16.5L x 16.5W x 21.5H

Form No: 1600-DO
No. Sold:

Med: 12L x 12.25W x 16.25H
Attached lid, knob towards front of lid, no handles.

E. 1990 – 1992 Heirloom

15L x 10W x 7.5H

Form No: 500-HOS
No. Sold:

I. 1992 – 1995 Gourmet Picnic

13.25L x 11.25W x 9H

Form No: 10413
No. Sold:

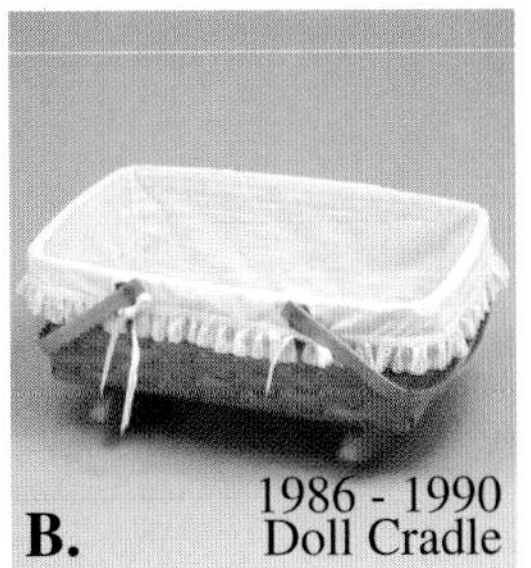

B. 1986 - 1990
Doll Cradle

19^L x 12^W x 6^H

Form No: 2500-LO
No. Sold:

Liner sold separately.

C. 1986 - 1990
Large Cradle

30^L x 20^W x 10.5^H

Form No: 2800-M
No. Sold:

Was not available with stain after 1984. Natural or natural with color only.

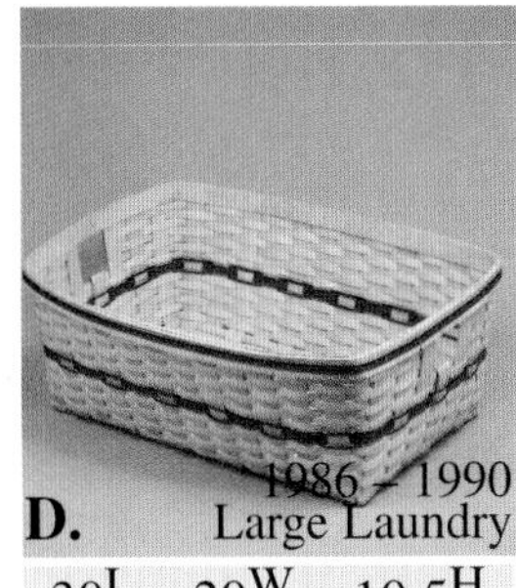

D. 1986 - 1990
Large Laundry

30^L x 20^W x 10.5^H

Form No: 2800-O
No. Sold:

Was not available with stain after 1984. Natural or natural with color only.

F. 1990 – 1992
Hearthside

11.75^{RD} x 6.5^H

Form No: 42000-AOS
No. Sold:

G. 1990 – 1992
Remembrance

10.5^L x 9^W x 8^H

Form No: 200-YOS
No. Sold:

H. 1990 – 1992
Harvest

16^L x 9^W x 6^H

Form No: 3700-AOS
No. Sold:

J. 1992 – 1996 Mail

12^L x 8^W x 11.5^H

Form No: 10600
No. Sold:

About the Hostess Collection . . .

Baskets from the Hostess Collection are only available to collectors who host basket parties. While the Hostess Collection was developed in 1986, the benefits available to hostesses have undergone many changes. Today, a Hostess must have a show of at least $125 in sales to qualify as a party. However, he or she must build their show to $250 in sales to be able to purchase a basket from the exclusive Hostess Collection. See a current *Wish List®* or your Consultant to find out what other benefits are available to you.

• Incentive Fun Facts •

The Longaberger Company® is known and appreciated for many things, bu nothing compares to how they treat their very own. Incentives and Awards have been a part of the very fabric of the company from day one. They seem to go above and beyond in letting their Consultants and Employees know that The Company would be nothing without them. This next sectio is all about appreciating and motivating their sales force, the Consultants.

Information about Incentives and Awards is extremely hard to collect because there have been so many and these prized possessions are rarely found on the secondary market. The items below are just a few of the ver rare Awards we were able to find . . .

Jewelr

A. Medallion necklace was given in 1992 to Top Sponsors.

B. This 14K Peg Basket charm matches the Bee Basket from 1994. It is also given to Top Sponsors.

C. Also given in 1992 to Top Sponsors, this 14K gold bracelet has a unique basket weave design. Each link has "Longaberger" engraved on the back.

D. This 14K Small Chore also mimics the 1995 Bee Basket and was a part of the Natl. Top Sponsoring Incentives.

A. B. C. D.

Miniatures

E. The Mini Discovery was given to 1992 Top Sponsors. All of these miniature award baskets were personally woven by Larry Longaberger.

F&G 1993 Top Sponsors received this Mini Cake, complete with a tiny divider. The open-weave bottom was a very familiar trait on baskets made by Larry.

H&I We have not been able to confirm these other two miniatures They were given as either High Sales or Top Sponsor awards. Years unknown.

Incentive / Award Baskets

Features:
Available only to Consultants, Advisors, & Sales Directors. Most have commemorative tags. No original prices associated with them.

Photo		Description	Original	Avg.	High
		Recruit / Sponsor Baskets:			
	1988	"Recruiting – Building Branches"			
		Sm.Fruit [WL] – 1 recruit		—	140
		Md. Fruit [WL] – 2 recruits		—	—
		Lg. Fruit [WL] – 3+ recruits		—	—
	1988	"Share the Tradition"			
A.	& 89	Recruit		170	220
B.		Sponsor		193	325
		Set:		—	425
	1990	"Together – We're Growing"			
C.		Recruit		169	180
D.		Sponsor		175	200
	1990	"Longaberger Rising Star"			
E.	& 91	Recruit		175	175
		Sponsor [np]		185	230
		*Superstar Sponsor [np]		155	200
	1992	"Flying High with Longaberger"			
F.		Recruit		119	125
G.		Sponsor (Large)		125	175
		*Sponsor (Small) [np]		118	175
	1993	"All-Star Recruiting"			
H.		Recruit		135	200
I.		Sponsor (Large)		130	165
		*Sponsor (Small) [np]		113	160
	1995	Longaberger Umbrella [np]		—	—
	1996	"Pegged for Your Success"		—	—
J.		Recruit		—	—
		with **P**rotector		—	—
		with **L**iner		—	—
		Combo **(P/L)**		--	—
		Sponsor [np]		—	—
		with **P**rotector		—	—
		with **L**iner		—	—
		Combo **(P/L)**			

KEY: [np] = Not Pictured

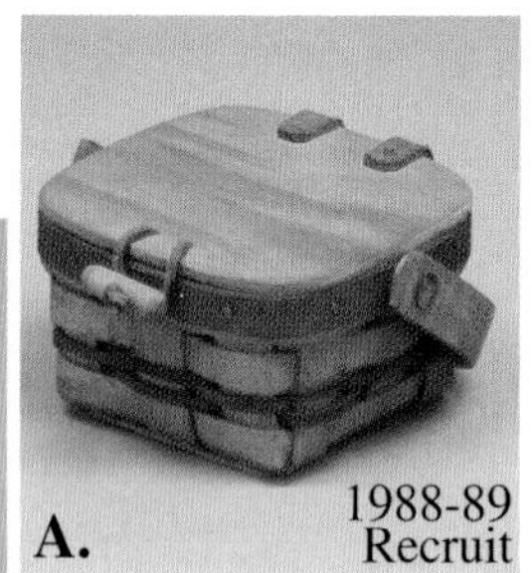

A. 1988-89 Recruit

5^L x 5^W x 2.5^H

Form No: 13000-BBRS
No. Given:

"Share the Tradition"
No tag on basket.

E. 1990-91 Recruit

12^L x 12.25^W x 16.25^H

Form No: 1700-DST
No. Given:

Superstar Sponsor: Same as above, except tag is different.
Sponsor (Lg.Hamper)
16.5L x 16.5W x 21.5H

I. 1993 Sponsor (Large)

8.25^L x 5^W x 3^H

Form No: 13323
No. Given:

"All-Star"

B. 1988-89 Sponsor

8.5^L x 8.5^W x 5^H

Form No: 1500-BBRS
No. Given:

"Share the Tradition"
No tag on basket.

C. 1990 Recruit

5.75^L x 3.75^W x 3^H

Form No: 45000-ABRST
No. Given:

Tag reads: "Together – 1990 Recruit"

D. 1990 Sponsor

9^L x 5^W x 5^H

Form No: 1100-ABRST
No. Given:

Tag reads: "Together – 1990 Sponsor"

F. 1992 Recruit

5RD x 4.5^H

Form No: 10154
No. Given:

NOTE: Basket in photo should have a brass tag.

G. 1992 Sponsor (Large)

7RD x 6.5^H

Form No: 10162
No. Given:

"Flying High with Longaberger"

1992 Sponsor (Small)
Looks the same as the 1992 Recruit, except tag is different

H. 1993 Recruit

8^L x 4^W x 2^H

Form No: 16101
No. Given:

"All-Star"

1993 Sponsor (Small)
Looks the same, except tag is different.

J. 1996 Recruit

5^L x 5^W x 4.5^H

Form No: unknown
No. Given:

"Pegged for Success"
Accessories could be earned with additional recruits.

• Basket Fun Facts •

"Pegged for Success" was a recruiting campaign during March 1996. Each Recruit during the period received the Small Peg. With one recruit, the Sponsor also received the Small Peg. When recruiting two people, the Sponsor earned both Peg baskets. Liners, lids and protectors for both baskets were given to the Sponsor when recruiting three or more.

Features:

All V.I.P. Baskets are the same size with 2 Sw/h.
No other basket shares this form.

MARKET VALUES

Photo		Description	Avg.	High
		National Sponsoring Awards:		
K.	1992	Green Trim and Weave	—	—
L.	1993	Red Trim and Weave		
		Sm.Gathering (5-9 recruits)	—	—
		Md. Gathering (10-14 recruits)	—	—
		Lg. Gathering (15-19 recruits)	—	—
		Lg. Gathering (20+ recruits)	—	—
M.	1994	Pink/Purple Trim and Weave		
		Sm.Gathering (5-9 recruits)	—	220
		Md. Gathering (10-14 recruits)	—	—
		Lg. Gathering (15-19 recruits)	—	—
		Lg. Gathering (20+ recruits)	—	—
N.	1995	Purple/Green Trim and Weave		
		Sm.Gathering (5-9 recruits)	—	—
		Md. Gathering (10-14 recruits)	—	—
		Lg. Gathering (15-19 recruits)	—	—
		Lg. Gathering (20+ recruits)	—	—
O.	1996	Blue/Gold/Red Trim and Weave		
		Sm.Gathering (5-9 recruits)	—	—
		Md. Gathering (10-14 recruits)	—	—
		Lg. Gathering (15-19 recruits)	—	—
		Lg. Gathering (20+ recruits)	—	—
		VIP – Honorable Mention:		
P.	1996	VIP Honorable Mention	—	—
		VIP – $30,000+ sales for the year:		
Q.	1986	Blue weave & trim	375	400
R.	1987	Green or Red weave & trim	363	400
S.	1988	Blue weave & trim	310	400
T.	1989	Red/Blue weave; Red trim	313	350
U.	1990	Pink/Blue weave; Pink trim	240	325
V.	1991	Blue weave & trim	310	425

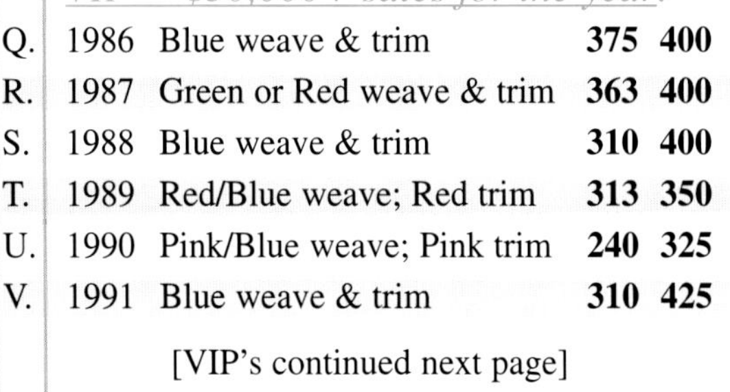

[VIP's continued next page]

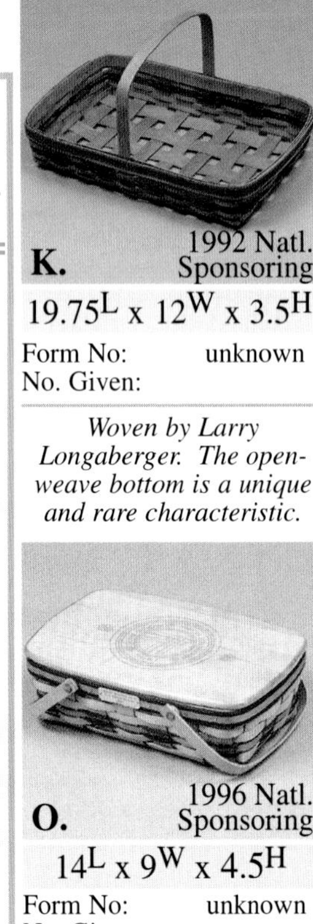

K. 1992 Natl. Sponsoring

19.75^L x 12^W x 3.5^H

Form No: unknown
No. Given:

Woven by Larry Longaberger. The open-weave bottom is a unique and rare characteristic.

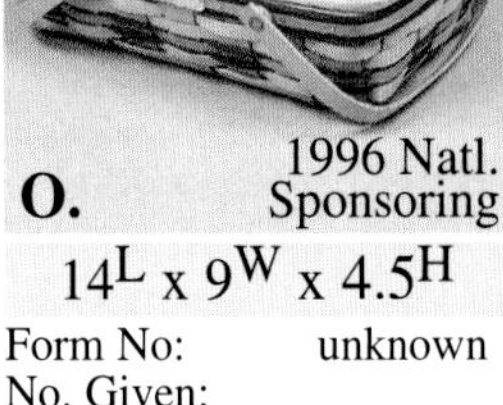

O. 1996 Natl. Sponsoring

14^L x 9^W x 4.5^H

Form No: unknown
No. Given:

Engraved lid included.

S. 1988 VIP

12^L x 7^W x 10^H

Form No: N/A
No. Given:

Selling Period: July 1987 – June 1988

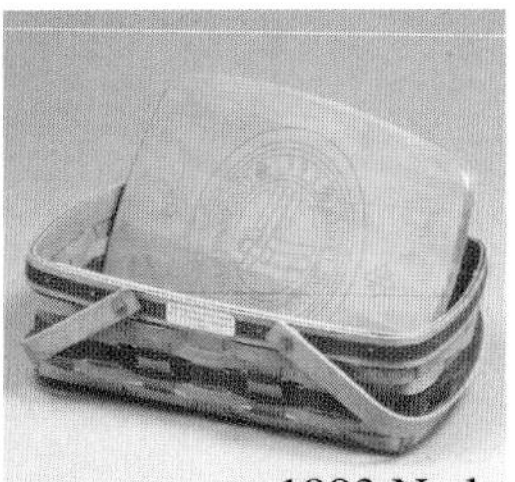

L. 1993 Natl. Sponsoring

14^{L} x 9^{W} x 4.5^{H}

Form No: unknown
No Given:

*Woven by Larry Longaberger. Unique open-weave bottom and **personalized** brass tag. Engraved lid included.*

M. 1994 Natl. Sponsoring

14^{L} x 9^{W} x 4.5^{H}

Form No: unknown
No Given:

Engraved lid included.

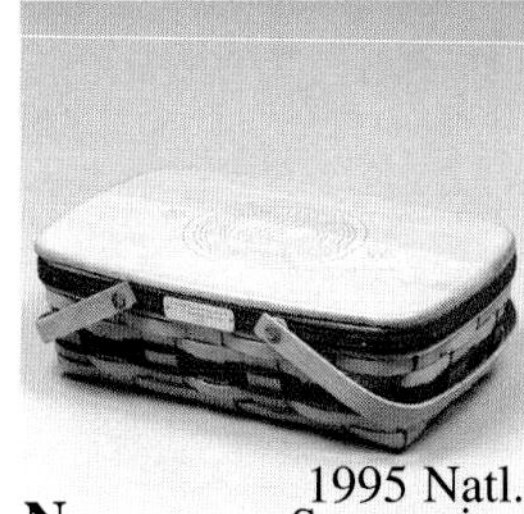

N. 1995 Natl. Sponsoring

19^{L} x 12^{W} x 6^{H}

Form No: unknown
No Given:

Engraved lid included.

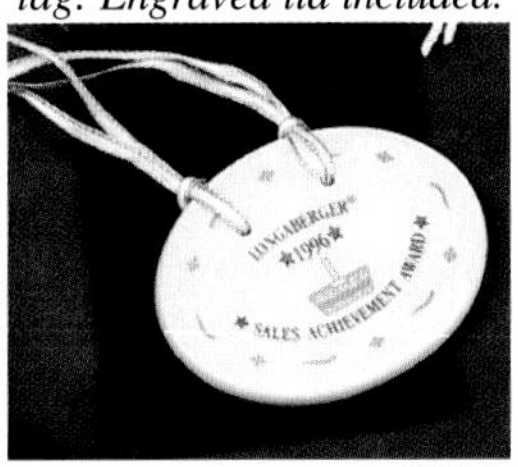

P. 1996 Honorable Mention

3RD x 2.5^{H}

Form No: N/A
No. Given:

Given to Consultants who attain $20,000 - $34,999 in sales.

Q. 1986 VIP

12^{L} x 7^{W} x 10^{H}

Form No: N/A
No. Given: 69

Selling Period:
Jan 1985 – Dec 1985

R. 1987 VIP

12^{L} x 7^{W} x 10^{H}

Form No: N/A
No. Given:

Selling Period:
Green: 1/86 – 6/86
Red: 7/86 – 6/87

T. 1989 VIP

12^{L} x 7^{W} x 10^{H}

Form No: N/A
No. Given:

Selling Period:
July 1988 – June 1989

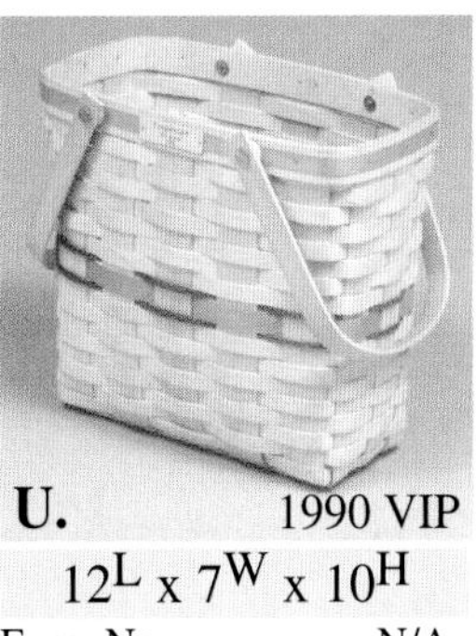

U. 1990 VIP

12^{L} x 7^{W} x 10^{H}

Form No: N/A
No. Given: 359

Selling Period:
July 1989 – June 1990

V. 1991 VIP

12^{L} x 7^{W} x 10^{H}

Form No: N/A
No. Given:

Selling Period:
July 1990 – June 1991

Features:

The V.I.P. Honorable Mention has been the only Tie-On given as an award.

Photo		Description		Avg.	High
		[VIP's continued from previous page]			
V.	1992	Green weave & trim		**270**	**340**
W.	1993	Teal/Pink weave; Teal trim		**285**	**350**
		VIP – $35,000+ sales for the year:			
X.	1994	Rose/Purple weave & trim		**210**	**220**
Y.	1995	Purple/Green weave & trim		—	—
Z.	1996	Blue/Gold/Green weave & trim		—	—
		National Sales Awards:			
A[1]	1983	Tin Punched Plaque		—	—
B[1]	1988	Coverlet Basket™		—	—
C[1]	1989	Flag Basket™		—	—
D[1]	1993	Red Trim and Weave			
		Sm.Fruit [np]	(Level 1)	—	—
		Md. Fruit	(Level 2)	—	—
		Lg. Fruit [np]	(Level 3)	—	—
E[1]	1994	Pink/Purple Trim and Weave			
		5" Measuring [np]	(Level 1)	—	—
		7" Measuring	(Level 2)	**168**	**185**
		9" Measuring[np]	(Level 3)	—	—
		11" Measuring [np]	(Level 4)	—	—
	1995	Purple/Green Trim and Weave			
		5" Measuring [np]	(Level 1)	—	—
		7" Measuring [np]	(Level 2)	—	—
		9" Measuring[np]	(Level 3)	—	—
		11" Measuring [np]	(Level 4)	—	—
F[1]	1996	Blue/Gold/Red Trim and Weave			
		5" Measuring	(Level 1)	—	—
		7" Measuring [np]	(Level 2)	—	—
		9" Measuring[np]	(Level 3)	—	—
		11" Measuring [np]	(Level 4)	—	—

KEY: [np] = Not Pictured

V. 1992 VIP

12L x 7W x 10H

Form No: N/A
No. Given:

Selling Period: July 1991 – June 1992

Z. 1996 VIP

12L x 7W x 10H

Form No: N/A
No. Given: 1356

Selling Period: July 1995 – June 1996

D1 1993 Natl. High Sales

8RD x 6.5H

Form No: unknown
No. Given:

$60,000 – 74,999 Sales in 1993.

W. 1993 VIP

$12^{L} \times 7^{W} \times 10^{H}$

Form No: N/A
No. Given:

Selling Period:
July 1992 – June 1993

X. 1994 VIP

$12^{L} \times 7^{W} \times 10^{H}$

Form No: N/A
No. Given:

Selling Period:
July 1993 – June 1994

Y. 1995 VIP

$12^{L} \times 7^{W} \times 10^{H}$

Form No: N/A
No. Given:

Selling Period:
July 1994 – June 1995

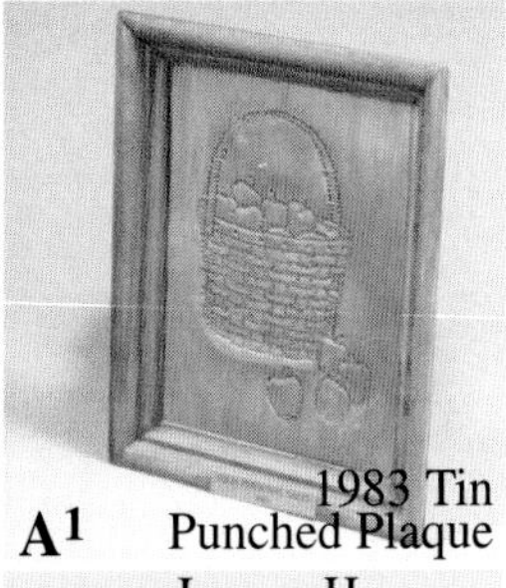

A1 1983 Tin Punched Plaque

$8^{L} \times 10^{H}$

Form No: N/A
No. Given: 35

Top selling consultants in 1983.

B1 1988 Coverlet

$16^{L} \times 16^{W} \times 8^{H}$

Form No: unknown
No. Given:

Top selling consultants in 1988.

C1 1989 Flag

$8.75^{L} \times 4.75^{W} \times 6.5^{H}$

Form No: unknown
No. Given:

Given to the Top selling Consultants during the "Weave Your American Dream" Bee in 1989.

E1 1994 Natl. High Sales

$7^{RD} \times 6.5^{H}$

Form No: unknown
No. Given:

$60,000 – 74,999 Sales in 1994.

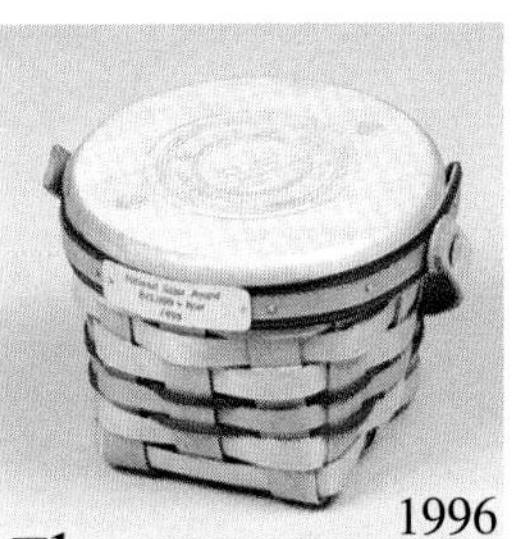

F1 1996 Natl. High Sales

$5^{RD} \times 4.5^{H}$

Form No: unknown
No. Given:

$45,000 – 59,999 Sales in 1996.

Features:

Baskets are not the only gifts given as Incentives and Awards. Commemorative Plates, Pottery, Jewelry and Trips are just a few examples of the other awards that have been given.

Photo		Description	MARKET VALUES Original	Avg.	High
		Miscellaneous Award and Incentives:			
G1	1985	Meadow Blossoms Pottery™	—		—
G1		Dinner Plates	—		—
G1		Mugs	—		—
G1		Napkin Rings	—		—
		Salad Plates [np]	—		—
		Sugar/Creamer Set [np]	—		—
H1		Pitcher	—		—
		Honey Pot [np]	—		—
		Soup Tureen [np]	—		—
		Soup Bowls [np]	—		—
		Buffet Trays [np]	—		—
		Oval Bowl [np]	—		—
		Piepan w/ Lattice Cover [np]	—		—
		Hurricane Lamp [np]	—		—
I1	1986	December Special Recognition* Bread Basket	145		175
J1	1986	Advisor Recognition Basket	—		95
	1987	10th Anniversary Recruiting Award "We're Building New Traditions"			
K1		Medium Market™	262		320
L1		Plate	154		200
		Candelabra [np]	—		—
	1987	May Basket			
M1		Herb™ (5 shows + $1000 sales)	80		80
	1988	May Incentive			
M1		Herb™ ($500 + 1 recruit)	80		80
		Garden™ [np] ($1000 + 1 recruit)	80		80
		Set:	142		175
N1	1991	Basket Planter Sleeve	445		500
	1992	"Success Start"			
O1	-pres.	Pencil Basket™	70		75
O1		Paper Basket™	65		75
		Set:	123		138
O1		Gold Pen	—		—
P1	1993	"Holiday Basket of Thanks"	72		110
Q1	1997	$500 Million Celebration	—		—

KEY: [np] = Not Pictured

G1 Meadow Blossoms 1985

Form No: N/A
No. Given:

Different groupings were available for each Recruit earned from 4/1/85 – 7/29/85

K1 Tenth Anniversary 1987

15^L x 10^W x 7.5^H

Form No: 500-A
No. Given:

Blue shoestring weave. Given for each new Recruit earned from 8/15 – 9/25/87.

O1 Success Start

Pencil: 15000-
Paper: 16000-
Pen: N/A

Consultants receive pen if reach $1000 in sales in first 90 days. Add Paper if achieve goal within 60 days, all three if within 30 days.

Logo Stamp on Bottom

H^1 Meadow Blossoms

See the "Basket Fun Facts" on page 126 for more information about Meadow Blossoms.

I^1 1986 December Recognition

$14.5^L \times 7.5^W \times 3.75^H$

Form No: 4700-AO
No. Given:

Sales of $500 or more for month of December. Signed by Dave.

J^1 1986 Advisor Recognition

$14^L \times 9^W \times 4.5^H$

Form No: 2300-
No. Given:

Given to all Advisors during a 1986 Meeting.

L^1 1987 Plate

Form No: N/A
No. Given: 660

Three $1000 months from Sept. – Nov.

M^1 1987 & 88 Herb

$11.5^L \times 5^W \times 3^H$

Form No: 4500-
No. Given:

Garden: $15^L \times 8^W \times 2.25^H$

N^1 1991 Planter Sleeve

$31.5^{RD} \times 18^H$

Form No: N/A
No. Given: 190

"High Road to Success"

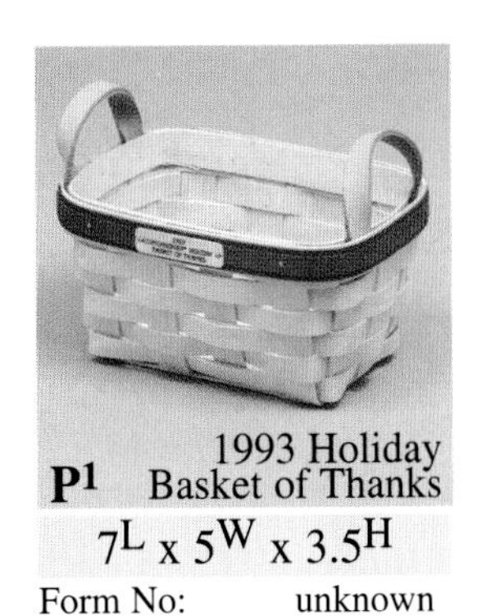

P^1 1993 Holiday Basket of Thanks

$7^L \times 5^W \times 3.5^H$

Form No: unknown
No. Given:

Red and green trim. Given for December Sales.

Q^1 1997 $500 Million

$10^L \times 6^W \times 4^H$

Form No: unknown
No. Given: ≈ 1,400

Given to all advisors at Jan 97 Advisor meeting to celebrate achieving $500 Million in Sales in Nov 96.

Features:
Bee Speaker baskets are given to those who volunteer their time at the Bee to speak to other consultants about various topics.

MARKET VALUES

Photo	Description		Avg.	High
	Bee Speaker Baskets:			
R1	1988	Medium Market™	—	—
S1	1990	Harvest™	—	—
T1	1991	Spring™	—	—
U1	1993	Spring™	223	245
V1	1994	Spring™	230	250
W1	1995	Spring™	—	—
X1	1996	Spring™	—	—
	Consultant Advancement Baskets:			
Y1	1988 – pres	MBA Basket™	198	220
Z1		Branch	300	312
A2		Regional	250	250
		Director [np]	—	—
	Branch Sponsored Awards:			
B2	1997	Branch Bouquet	—	—

• Market Fun Facts •

A recent trend in the Secondary Market has been the buying and selling of paperwork: Longaberger promo flyers, Wish Lists®, product cards, everything. Some collectors have even started keeping the kraft paper that their baskets are delivered in to stress the point that they have kept their basket in the original, "mint" condition

KEY: [np] = Not Pictured

R1 1988 Bee Speaker

15L x 10W x 7.5H

Form No: 500-
No. Given: 15

Blue shoestring weave.

V1 1994 Bee Speaker

11L x 8W x 5.5H

Form No: 900-
No. Given:

Pink and purple trim and weave.

Z1 Branch Advisor

15.75L x 6.5W x 11H

Form No: unknown

No tag.

S^1 1990 Bee Speaker

16^L x 9^W x 6^H

Form No: 3700-
No. Given:

No color. Brass tag.

T^1 1991 Bee Speaker

11^L x 8^W x 5.5^H

Form No: 900-
No. Given:

Blue trim and weave.

U^1 1993 Bee Speaker

11^L x 8^W x 5.5^H

Form No: 900-
No. Given:

Teal and pink weave and trim.

W^1 1995 Bee Speaker

11^L x 8^W x 5.5^H

Form No: 900-
No. Given:

Purple and green trim and weave.

X^1 1996 Bee Speaker

11^L x 8^W x 5.5^H

Form No: 900-
No. Given:

Blue, gold and red trim and weave.

Y^1 MBA

9.5^L x 5^W x 9.5^H

Form No: 1000-FO
No. Given:

No tag.

A^2 Regional Advisor

15.75^L x 6.5^W x 11^H

Form No: unknown
No. Given:

Director: Green Weaving

B^2 1997 Branch Bouquet

10.5^L x 6^W x 4^H

Form No: unknown
No. Given:

First year for a Branch Advisor to sponsor an award.

Features:

The Regional Sponsored Awards are funded and given out by each Regional Advisor. The number of awards given out is determined by the size of their Region.

Photo	Description		Avg.	High
	Regional Sponsored Awards:			
C2	1991	Small Chore	**175**	**200**
D2	1992	Small Oval	**195**	**275**
E2	1993	Potpourri with Lid	**187**	**275**
F2	1994	Small Purse, no Lid	**226**	**250**
G2	1995	Medium Berry	**234**	**250**
H2	1996	Darning	**190**	**210**
I2	1997	Rose Garden	—	—
	Director Sponsored Awards:			
J2	1991	Pom Pom Peggy™	—	—
K2	1992	Treasure Chest™	**197**	**275**
L2	1992	Top Performer	**198**	**200**
M2	1993	Paint the Town™	**119**	**185**
N2	1993	Top Performer	—	**200**

(Avg. and High are MARKET VALUES.)

About Director Sponsored Awards . . .

1991 was the first year for these awards. They are developed, funded and given out by the individual Sales Directors and usually are given in four categories:

[1] Those achieving 4+ recruits

[2] Those doing 50 or more shows

[3] Branch Advisors who have 30% of their Branch achieving the 50+ shows award

[4] Top 10 Performers under their Directorship.

C2 1991 Regional Sponsored

10L x 6W x 4H

Form No: 3400-
No. Given:

Blue weave and trim. Given for High Sales in the Region.

G2 1995 Regional Sponsored

7.5L x 7.5W x 3.5H

Form No: 1400-
No. Given:

Blue trim and weave. Braided ears.

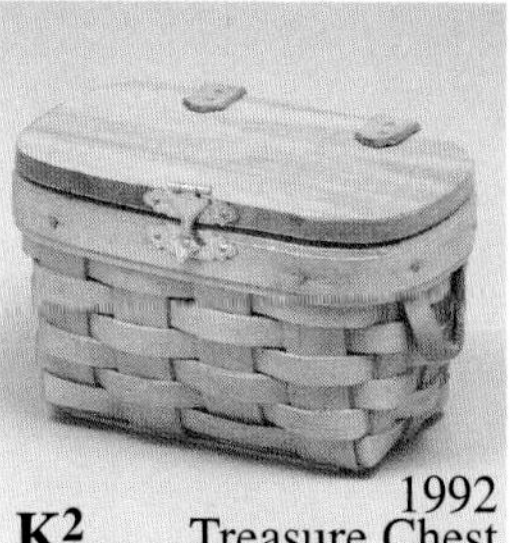

K2 1992 Treasure Chest

5.75L x 3.75W x 3H

Form No: 45000-
No. Given:

Given to consultants with 50+ shows.

D^2 1992 Regional Sponsored

$8^{L} \times 5^{W} \times 3^{H}$

Form No: 33000-
No. Given:

Green, blue and red shoestring weave.

E^2 1993 Regional Sponsored

$5^{L} \times 5^{W} \times 2.5^{H}$

Form No: 11321
No. Given:

Blue weave and trim.

F^2 1994 Regional Sponsored

$9.5^{L} \times 6^{W} \times 6^{H}$

Form No: 800-
No. Given:

Blue trim and shoe-string weave. Two braided ears.

H^2 1996 Regional Sponsored

$10^{RD} \times 4^{H}$

Form No: 500-
No. Given:

Red trim and shoe-string weave at bottom.

I^2 1997 Regional Sponsored

$12^{L} \times 7^{W} \times 4.5^{H}$

Form No: unknown
No. Given:

Green trim and shoe-string accent weave.

J^2 Pom Pom Peggy

12^{H}

First Director Sponsored Award. Received doll for 50+ shows . The basket charm attached at her neck was could be earned with 1 recruit.

L^2 1992 Top Performer

$10.5^{L} \times 9^{W} \times 8^{H}$

Form No: unknown
No. Given:

Green, blue, and red weave. Top 10 Consultants in the Directorship.

M^2 1993 Paint the Town

$5.75^{L} \times 3.75^{W} \times 3^{H}$

Form No: 45000-
No. Given:

Green, blue, and red weave. 50+ shows.

N^2 1993 Top Performer

$10.5^{L} \times 9^{W} \times 8^{H}$

Form No: unknown
No. Given:

Green, blue, and red weave. Top 10 consultants in the Directorship.

Features:
The Director Sponsored award, Top Performer, is the same as the High Achiever. When the shape of the basket was changed in 1991, it was renamed as well.

MARKET VALUES

Photo		Description	Avg.	High
O2	1994	"Over the Rainbow"		
		Gold Nugget (Small)	178	235
		Pot of Gold (Medium)	129	160
		Gold Rush (Large)	165	270
P2		Top Performer	267	350
	1995	"Reach for the Stars"		
Q2		Star Bound (Small)	215	300
R2		Shining Star (Medium)	185	300
S2		Star Team (Large)	219	300
T2		High Achiever	—	275
	1996	"Our Business is Show Business"		
U2		Associate Producer (Small)	—	—
V2		Show Star (Medium)	118	160
W2		Best Supporting Role (Large)	105	150
X2		High Achiever	—	—
	1997	"Everything's Coming Up Roses"		
		Rose Bud (Small)[np]	—	—
Y2		Rose Pedal (Medium)	—	—

[continued on next page]

KEY: [np] = Not Pictured

1994
O2 Over the Rainbow
Form No: unknown

Small: *4.5RD x 3H*
4+ recruits
Medium: *5.5RD x 3.75H*
50+ shows
Large: *6.5RD x 4.75H*
$40,000+ sales

S2 1995 Star Team

7L x 5W x 3.5H

Form No: unknown
No. Given:

Available only to Branch Advisors when 30% of their Branch achieves the Shining Star.

W2 1996 Best Supporting Role

8.5RD x 4H

Form No:
No. Given:

Awarded to Branch Advisors when 30% of their Branch achieves the Show Star.

P2 1994 Top Performer

10.5^L x 9^W x 8^H

Form No: unknown
No. Given:

Teal Weave; Top 10 consultants in the Directorship.

Q2 1995 Star Bound

4.75^L x 3.75^W x 2.25^H

Form No: unknown
No. Given:

4+ recruits

R2 1995 Shining Star

5.75^L x 3.75^W x 3^H

Form No: unknown
No. Given:

50+ shows

T2 1995 High Achiever

12RD x 5.75^H

Form No: unknown
No. Given:

Top 10 consultants

U2 1996 Associate Producer

5.5^{RD} x 2.5^H

Form No:
No. Given:

4+ Recruits

V2 1996 Show Star

7RD x 3^H

Form No:
No. Given:

50+ shows

X2 1996 High Achiever

12RD x 5.75^H

Form No:
No. Given:

Top 10 Consultants in the Directorship.

Y2 1997 Rose Petal

8.5^L x 5^W x 3.5^H

Form No:
No. Given:

50+ shows

Features:
The "theme" for the Director Sponsored Awards are developed by actual Consultants well over a year before they are actually awarded.

MARKET VALUES

Photo	Description	Avg.	High
	"Everything's Coming Up Roses" [con't]		
Z2	Rose Bud Flower Pots	—	—
A3	American Beauty	—	—

Z2 1997 Rose Bud Pots

2.5^{RD} x 2.5^{H}

Form No: 33693
No. Given:

Available only to Branch Advisors when 30% of their Branch achieves the 50+ shows.

A3 1997 American Beauty

13.5^{L} x 8.25^{W} x 5.25^{H}

Form No:
No. Given:

Top 10 Consultants in the Directorship.

• *Incentive Fun Facts* •

G.S.T. Basket
9.5^{L} x 5^{W} x 9.5^{H}

Throughout the year, The Longaberger Company puts on special training for their new Branch Advisors. This training is called "Growing Strong Together" [G.S.T.] and takes place at The Longaberger University in Dresden, Ohio usually once, sometimes twice a month. This three day training is free to new Branch Advisors and is facilitated with the help of Regional Advisors and Directors. As a thank you for sharing their time and expertise, these Facilitators receive this GST Basket. It's unique yellow and green trim is not seen on any other basket produced by The Company. Although quantities are uncertain, it is estimated that approximately 2-3 Facilitators attend each training.

J.W. Collection®

Features:
Blue Accent Weave and Trim.
Commemorative Brass Tag.
Series Retired in 1994.

MARKET VALUES

Photo	Description	Original	Avg.	High
A.	1983 Market™	32.95	**1211**	**1550**
B.	1984 Waste™	34.95	**1031**	**1300**
C.	1985 Apple™	45.95	**609**	**800**
D.	1986 Two-Pie™	34.95	**480**	**650**
E.	1987 Bread and Milk™	43.95	**390**	**550**
	with **P**rotector		**—**	**—**
	with **L**iner (1993)		**—**	**—**
	Combo **(P/L)**		**425**	**550**
F.	1988 Gathering™	36.95	**282**	**500**
G.	1989 Banker's Waste™	59.95	**276**	**400**
H.	1990 Large Berry™	48.95	**172**	**230**
	Combo **(P)**	53.90	**180**	**280**
I.	1991 Corn™	89.95	**325**	**425**
	Combo **(P)**	103.90	**330**	**480**
J.	1992 Cake™	55.95	**155**	**210**
	with **P**rotector	65.90	**168**	**210**
	with **L**iner	67.90	**168**	**210**
	Combo **(P/L)**	69.95	**175**	**250**
K.	1993 Original Easter™	65.95	**153**	**200**
	with **P**rotector	71.90	**161**	**210**
	with **L**iner	83.90	**161**	**210**
	Combo **(P/L)**	82.95	**165**	**220**
L.	1994 Umbrella™	74.95	**143**	**245**
	Combo **(P)**	79.95	**150**	**250**
L.	1994 JW Commemorative Book	24.95	**25**	**49**

Full Set JW Collection: — **5000**

A. 1983 Market

$15^L \times 10^W \times 7.5^H$

Form No: 500-AT
No. Sold: 6,300

E. 1987 Bread and Milk

$16^L \times 8^W \times 11^H$

Form No: 2100-ABT
No. Sold: 17,818

Did not originally sell with accessories. Liner first offered in 1993. Magazine protector used from the regular line.

I. 1991 Corn

$17^{RD} \times 11.5^H$

Form No: 4400-JBST
No. Sold: 48,332

You MUST send us this form

to receive the Six Month Update that was included in the price of this Fifth Edition Bentley Collection Guide®.

Who needs to register for the Six Month Update?

Everyone! It doesn't matter if you bought the Guide directly from J. Phillip, bought it through a Retail Store, or from your Advisor, it is necessary for **every-one** to send in this registration to receive the Update automatically and at no additional cost. Even those who bought the Three Year Subscription of the Guide **must** send in this registration to receive the Fifth Edition Update.

When do I need to send in this registration?

Right away. You can send it as soon as you open your Guide, just be sure to send us your winter address. In order to get your Update ***without delay***, you must **send it in by November 30, 1997**.

What if I miss the deadline?

If you have purchased the Guide after this deadline, the Six Month Update should be packaged with the other shrink wrapped items that came with it. **Please still send in this card so that you will be notified of any changes or new editions to the Guide.** If you are missing this update, first contact the store or person from whom you purchased it. If they purchased your Guide before this deadline, it will not have the Update. Call us at 1-800-837-4394 with proof of your purchase: receipt or cancelled check.

When can I expect the Six Month Update?

For those who register before the deadline, this year the Updates will be mailied via First Class Mail by January 1998. If you register after the deadline, there will be a cost of $2.95 for your Update and postage.

How to fill out the registration . . .

(1) Fill-in all of the requested information
(2) Tear this page out of your Guide
(3) Fold the page in half, with your address information on the inside
(4) Tape closed
(5) Put a first class stamp on the front
(6) Put into the mail

Please Print

❒ New Address (as of:_______) ❒ Do not exchange my name

❒ Collector ❒ Consultant (Circle: MBA / Branch / Reg / Dir)

Bentley Cust. #: ______________________

Name: ______________________

Address: ______________________

____

City: ______________ State:______ Zip: __________

Day Phone: ( ) ____________ Evening: ____________

Which Edition(s) of the Bentley Guide do you have?

❒ All Five ❒ 1st (93) ❒ 2nd (94) ❒ 3rd (95) ❒ 4th (96) ❒ 5th (97)

Where did you purchase this year's Edition of the Guide?

❒ From Bentley directly ❒ From a Consultant ❒ Through an Advisor

❒ From a Retail Store ❒ At an Auction ❒ Other: ____________

Fold in half

Place
Stamp
Here

The Bentley Collection Guide®

c/o J. Phillip, Incorporated
5870 Zarley Street, Suite C
New Albany, OH 43054-9700

[tape closed]

B. 1984 Waste

$9.5^L \times 9.5^W \times 12^H$

Form No: 1800-OT
No. Sold: 3,544

C. 1985 Apple

$13^{RD} \times 8.5^H$

Form No: 3200-BT
No. Sold: 10,467

Also referred to as a Large Fruit.

D. 1986 Two-Pie

$12^L \times 12^W \times 10^H$

Form No: 4800-BT
No. Sold: 44,363

F. 1988 Gathering

$18^L \times 11^W \times 4.5^H$

Form No: 2400-ABT
No. Sold: 49,495

G. 1989 Banker's Waste

$12.5^{RD} \times 13.5^H$

Form No: 1900-BBST
No. Sold: 53,328

H. 1990 Large Berry

$8.5^L \times 8.5^W \times 5^H$

Form No: 1500-BBST
No. Sold: 37,009

J. 1992 Cake

$12^L \times 12^W \times 6^H$

Form No: 100-CBST
No. Sold: 98,557

Basket sold with divider.

K. 1993 Original Easter

$16^L \times 9^W \times 6^H$

Form No: 13722
No. Sold: ≈ 77,000

L. 1994 Umbrella

$10^{RD} \times 17.5^H$

Form No: 11215
Book: 72214
No. Sold: ≈ 95,000

Book sold separately.

• Family Fun Facts •

J.W. Longaberger was born in 1902. He left high school at age 17 to help his father make baskets full-time. He married Bonnie Jean Gist (Grandma Bonnie) in 1927. They had twelve children between 1928 and 1945. J.W. continued making baskets while he worked during the day at the Dresden Paper Mill. He sold each basket for about $1.50. Dave Longaberger joined his father making baskets in 1972. J.W. had since stopped making baskets for sale, but agreed to make a few for Dave to sell. J.W. passed away at age 71 before The Longaberger Company® was established.

Bonnie Jean
"Grandma Bonnie
Born:
July 16, 190

The Longaberger Children:

#1 Genevieve
Born: Mar. 25, 1928
Spouse: Piercy Hard

#2 Wendy Jean
Born: Dec. 16, 1929
Spouse: Bob Little

#3 Jerry Dean
Born: Nov. 23, 1931
Spouse: Donna

#4 Dale "Larry"
Born: June 3, 1933

#5 David Wendell
Born: Dec. 7, 1934

#6 Richard Lee
Born: Dec. 18, 1936
Spouse: Joanne

#7 Maryann
Born: Nov. 29, 1937
Spouse:
Wendell McCafferty

#8 Judy Kay
Born: Sept. 19, 1939

#9 "Ginny" Lou
Born: Oct. 8, 1940
Spouse: Dick Wilcox

#10 Gary Conway
Born: Jan. 6, 1943

#11 Carmen Lynn
Born: Nov. 23, 1943
Spouse: Ronald Fortney

#12 Jeff Carl
Born: Mar. 11, 1945
Spouse: Jane

Dave's Children:

#1 Tami Lynne
Spouse: Mike Kaido

#2 Rachel Lynne
Spouse: Doug Schmidt

May Series™

Features:

Named after Grandma Bonnie's Favorite Flowers

Photo	Description	Original	Avg.	High
A.	1990 Violet™	24.95	**165**	**250**
	with **P**rotector	28.90	**180**	**250**
	with **L**iner	34.90	**185**	**250**
	Combo **(P/L)**	34.95	**238**	**375**
B.	1991 Rose™	29.95	**137**	**235**
	with **P**rotector	34.90	**156**	**250**
	with **L**iner	41.90	**156**	**250**
	Combo **(P/L)**	39.95	**182**	**285**
C.	1992 Pansy™	29.95	**86**	**125**
	with **P**rotector	34.90	**86**	**125**
	with **L**iner	41.90	**86**	**125**
	Combo **(P/L)**	39.95	**116**	**185**
D.	1993 Lily of the Valley™	28.95	**60**	**80**
	with **P**rotector	32.90	**75**	**80**
	with **L**iner	41.90	**75**	**80**
	Combo **(P/L)**	39.95	**80**	**135**
E.	1994 Lilac™	34.95	**80**	**105**
	with **P**rotector	39.95	**80**	**105**
	with **L**iner	47.90	**80**	**105**
	Combo **(P/L)**	42.95	**88**	**130**
E.	1994 Lilac™ Tie-On	5.95	**17**	**35**
F.	1995 Tulip™	42.95	**78**	**100**
	with **P**rotector	48.90	**80**	**100**
	with **L**iner	57.90	**80**	**100**
	Combo **(P/L)**	54.95	**83**	**125**
F.	1995 Tulip™ Tie-On	6.95	**11**	**15**
G.	1996 Sweet Pea™	45.95	**60**	**75**
	with **P**rotector	52.90	**60**	**75**
	with **L**iner	61.90	**60**	**75**
	Combo **(P/L)**	59.95	**76**	**100**
G.	1996 Sweet Pea™ Tie-On	6.95	**10**	**15**
H.	1997 Petunia™	45.95	—	—
	with **P**rotector	52.90	—	—
	with **L**iner	63.90	—	—
	Combo **(P/L)**	59.95	—	—
	with **Lid**	74.90	—	—
	Full Set **(Combo/Lid)**	88.90	—	—
H.	1997 Petunia™ Tie-On	6.95	—	—

A. 1990 Violet

5^L x 5^W x 4.5^H

Form No: 14000-BVS
No. Sold: 49,591

There were 28,791 Combos sold this year.

E. 1994 Lilac

6.5^{RD} x 6.5^H

Form No: 16209
Tie-On: 31291
No. Sold:

Tie-On sold separately.

B. 1991 Rose

14.5^{L} x 7.5^{W} x 3.75^{H}

Form No: 4700-CSS
No. Sold:

C. 1992 Pansy

7RD x 4.5^{H}

Form No: 10006
No. Sold:

D. 1993 Lily of the Valley

5.5RD x 3.75^{H}

Form No: 15717
No. Sold:

3/8" Weaving. No color. Does not have an inverted bottom.

F. 1995 Tulip

14.25^{L} x 6.25^{W} x 3.25^{H}

Form No: 14648
Tie-On: 31542
No. Sold:

Tie-On sold separately.

G. 1996 Sweet Pea

8.25RD x 7^{H}

Form No: 14915
Tie-On: 32883
No. Sold:

Tie-On sold separately.

H. 1997 Petunia

9.5RD x 5^{H}

Form No: 12947
Tie-On: 34461
No. Sold:

Tie-On sold separately.

• *Grandma Bonnie Fun Facts* •

- Grandma Bonnie was the first Collectors Club™ Member
- Bonnie always refers to J.W. as "Wendell"
- She grew up in a town called Trinway, Ohio
- NEXT YEAR, she will be *90 years old* on July 16, 1998

• Basket Fun Facts •

The Tea Basket™ has had an interesting history with The Company. It is the single most common form used as it shows up in over 25 different ways represented in almost half of the collections, including the Regular Line.

It has been a part of the Regular Line since the beginning. Originally the Mini Berry, it was renamed the Tea Basket on May 1, 1991 when The Company heard on "good authority" that the Queen of England was using the basket to hold her own tea bags.

The Tea form was first featured in a collection in 1987 with the Christmas Mistletoe™ with the most recent appearance being made in the 1997 All-American Patriot™. This basket looks so good any way that it is dressed, it is almost hard to recognize that it is a Tea Basket. Test your Tea Basket™ knowledge with the following challenge:

Match the Collection Name with the Tea Basket "disguise" that fits the basket found in that collection:

All-American	1 sw/h, lid
Easter	1 sw/h, lengthwise
Employee	1 st/h, across width
Incentive	1 sw/h, shoestring weaving
Retired	two ears

[look for the answers below]

Tea Basket™ Timeline:

1979 - 87	Regular Line	Baby Easter™
1979 - 91	Regular Line	Mini Berry™
1979 - 93	Regular Line	Mini Cradle™
1979 - P	Regular Line	Mini Chore™
1979 - P	Regular Line	Small Key™
1979 - P	Regular Line	Kiddie Purse™
1991 - P	Regular Line	Tea ™
1987	Christmas	Mistletoe™
1988	Easter	Baby Easter™
1989	Mother's Day	Mini Chore™
1989 - P	Regular Line	Heartland Mini Chore™
1991	Easter	Hostess™
1993	Easter	Small Easter™
1994	Feature	Small Key™
1994	Regular Line	Natural Kiddie Purse™
1994	Employee	Christmas Tea™
1994	Incentive	Holiday Basket of Thanks™
1994 - P	Regular Line	Heartland Small Key™
1995	Incentive	Director Sponsored Star Team™
1995 - P	Regular Line	Woven Traditions Tea™
1997	All-American®	Patriot™

nswers: All-American = 1 sw/h, lengthwise (Patriot); Easter = 1 st/h, across width
ll); Employee = 1 sw/h, shoestring weaving (94 Christmas); Incentive = two ears
ll); Retired = 1 sw/h, lid (Kiddie Purse)

Mother's Day™

Features:

Pink Weave and Trim, except in 1993.

Photo		Description	Original	Avg.	High
A.	1987	Large Peg™	26.95	**119**	**160**
B.	1988	Spring™	28.95	**130**	**170**
		Combo **(L)**	39.90	**134**	**170**
C.	1989	Mini Chore™	21.95	**85**	**150**
		Combo **(L)**	29.95	**100**	**150**
D.	1990	Small Oval™	28.95	**75**	**100**
		Combo **(L)**	36.95	**100**	**110**
E.	1991	Purse™	34.95	**115**	**150**
		with **P**rotector	39.90	**115**	**150**
		with **L**iner	49.90	**115**	**150**
		Combo **(P/L)**	54.85	**120**	**150**
F.	1991	Potpourri™	21.95	**71**	**110**
		Combo **(L)**	30.90	**80**	**125**
G.	1992	Mother's Day™	34.95	**76**	**125**
		with **P**rotector	40.90	**80**	**125**
		with **L**iner	50.90	**80**	**125**
		Combo **(P/L)**	49.95	**94**	**140**
H.	1993	Mother's Day™	44.95	**89**	**115**
		with **P**rotector	50.90	**100**	**115**
		with **L**iner	59.90	**100**	**115**
		Combo **(P/L)**	57.95	**115**	**130**
I.	1994	Mother's Day™	37.95	**72**	**95**
		with **P**rotector	42.90	**72**	**100**
		with **L**iner	50.90	**72**	**100**
		Combo **(P/L)**	49.95	**75**	**115**
I.	1994	Mother's Journal	5.95	**10**	**15**
J.	1995	Mother's Day™	37.95	**67**	**80**
		with **P**rotector	43.90	**67**	**80**
		with **L**iner	52.90	**67**	**80**
		Combo **(P/L)**	49.95	**70**	**100**
J.	1995	Mother's Day Tie-On	6.95	**10**	**15**
K.	1996	Mother's Day™	44.95	**65**	**100**
		with **P**rotector	56.90	—	—
		with **L**iner	60.90	—	—
		Combo **(P/L)**	59.95	**79**	**110**
		with **Lid**	67.90	—	—
		Full Set **(Combo/Lid)**	82.90	**95**	**110**
K.	1996	Mother's Day Tie-On	6.95	**12**	**15**
L.	1997	Timeless Memory™	49.95	—	—
		with **P**rotector	59.90	—	—
		with **L**iner	69.90	—	—
		Combo **(P/L)**	69.95	—	—
		with **Lid**	72.90	—	—
		Full Set **(Combo/Lid)**	92.90	—	—
L.	1997	Mother's Day Tie-On	6.95	—	—

A. 1987 Large Peg

6.5L x 6.5W x 8H

Form No: 11000-BPS
No. Sold:

E. 1991 Purse

9.5L x 6W x 6H

Form No: 800-EPS
No. Sold:

I. 1994 Mother's Day

6.75L x 9.25W x 3.75H

Form No: 16004
Journal: 72087
No. Sold:

Journal sold separately.

B. 1988 Spring

11^{L} x 8^{W} x 5.5^{H}

Form No: 900-APS
No. Sold:

Promotion did not include a Combo.

C. 1989 Mini Chore

7^{L} x 5^{W} x 3.5^{H}

Form No: 700-APS
No. Sold:

Included note cards.

D. 1990 Small Oval

8.5^{L} x 5^{W} x 3.5^{H}

Form No: 33000-JPS
No. Sold:

Promotion did not include a Combo.

F. 1991 Potpourri

5^{L} x 5^{W} x 2.5^{H}

Form No: 13000-APS
No. Sold:

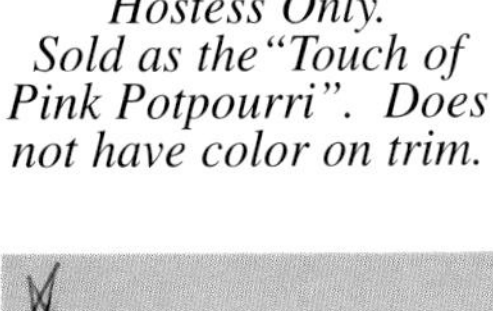

Hostess Only. Sold as the "Touch of Pink Potpourri". Does not have color on trim.

G. 1992 Mother's Day

10.5^{L} x 10.5^{W} x 4.5^{H}

Form No: 110-CPS
No. Sold:

H. 1993 Mother's Day

8.5^{L} x 8^{W} x 6^{H}

Form No: 12904
No. Sold:

3/8" Weaving. No color.

J. 1995 Mother's Day

8.5^{RD} x 4^{H}

Form No: 18805
Tie-On: 31470
No. Sold:
Tie-On: 90,515

Tie-On sold separately

K. 1996 Mother's Day

13.5^{L}x 7.5^{W}x 4.5^{FH}x6.5^{BH}

Form No: 14753
Tie-On: 32328
No. Sold: 224,278

Tie-On & Lid sold separately. Divided protector came with Combo. A regular protector also available for $5.95.

L. 1997 Timeless Memory

11.25^{L} x 9.25^{W} x 5.75^{H}

Form No: 63029
Tie-On: 33995
No. Sold:

Tie-On & Lid sold separately

• Basket Fun Facts •

Large Hamper Basket History . . .

The Large Hamper™ is a form that has shown up in the Longaberger product line in many different variations. Following is a brief history time line describing the different looks of the Large Hamper.

Prior to 1979 – July, 1986

- Available through the Regular Line.
- Attached Woven Lid with knob <u>at front</u> of Lid.
- No hand slots.
- Darker "old" stain, Natural or Natural with color.

August, 1986 – 1990

- Available through the Hostess Collection.
- Attached Woven Lid with knob <u>at front</u> of Lid.
- No hand slots.
- Darker "old" stain, Natural or Natural with color.
- After 1987: Lighter "new" stain <u>only.</u>

May 1986

- Available as a Feature Basket.
- No Lid.
- First time for two hand slots.
- Darker "old" stain <u>only</u>.

1991

- Available through the Hostess Collection for one month to Shades of Autumn Hostesses only.
- 3/8" Hostess Weaving.
- Detached Woven Lid with knob in <u>middle</u> of Lid.
- Two hand slots.
- Lighter "new" stain <u>only.</u>

1993 – 1994

- Available through the Regular Line.
- Detached Woven Lid with knob in middle of Lid.
- Two hand slots.
- Lighter "new" stain <u>only.</u>

1995 – present (See Wish List™)

- Available through the Hostess Collection.
- 3/8" Hostess Weaving.
- Detached Woven Lid with knob in middle of Lid.
- Two hand slots.
- Lighter "new" stain <u>only.</u>

Prior to 1979 – 1990
Large Hamper

1986 Feature Hamper

1991 Shades of Autum
Hostess Hamper

1993 – 1994 Hamper looks just like this exce 1/2" weave. Returned 3/8" weave in 1995 Hostess Collection.

Pewter Ornaments

Features:

Available individually or in sets of four.
Each ornament approximately 2" high.

Photo	Description	Original	Avg.	High
A.	*1993 Commemorative Santa Collection*			
	Father Christmas™	8.95	**10**	**12**
	Kriss Kringle™	8.95	**10**	**12**
	Santa Claus™	8.95	**10**	**12**
	St. Nick™	8.95	**10**	**12**
	SET of Four Gift Set	29.95	**60**	**105**
B.	*1994 Commemorative Baskets Collection*			
	1981 Candle™	8.95	—	—
	1982 Sleigh™	8.95	—	—
	1983 Bell™	8.95	—	—
	1984 Holly™	8.95	—	—
	SET of Four Gift Set	29.95	**54**	**95**
C.	*1995 Commemorative Baskets Collection*			
	1985 Cookie™	8.95	—	—
	1986 Candy Cane™	8.95	—	—
	1987 Mistletoe™	8.95	—	—
	1988 Poinsettia™	8.95	—	—
	SET of Four Gift Set	29.95	**48**	**60**
D.	*1996 Commemorative Baskets Collection*			
	1989 Memory™	8.95	—	—
	1990 Gingerbread™	8.95	—	—
	1991 Yuletide Traditions™	8.95	—	—
	1992 Season's Greetings™	8.95	—	—
	SET of Four Gift Set	29.95	—	—

1993
A. Santa Ornaments
Form No:

Father Christmas	70653
Kriss Kringle	70637
Santa Claus	70629
St.Nick	70645
SET	70661

1994
B. Basket Ornaments
Form No:

Candle	72273
Sleigh	72281
Bell	72290
Holly	72303
SET	72311

1995
C. Basket Ornaments
Form No:

Cookie	72141
Candy Cane	71838
Mistletoe	71943
Poinsettia	72460
SET	71803

1996
D. Basket Ornaments
Form No:

Memory	71951
Gingerbread	72028
Yuletide Traditions	72001
Season's Greetings	71935
SET	71901

Pottery®

Features:

Roseville: Produced by Friendship Pottery from 1990 – 91.

Photo	Description	Original	Avg.	High
	Roseville Pottery			
A.	Small Mixing Bowl	17.95	**40**	**65**
A.	Medium Mixing Bowl	22.95	**48**	**80**
A.	Large Mixing Bowl	29.95	**57**	**80**
B.	Grandma Bonnie's Apple Pie Plate	23.95	**50**	**85**
C.	Small Juice Pitcher	21.95	**50**	**70**
C.	Large Milk Pitcher	27.95	**62**	**89**
	Full Set		**225**	**250**

(MARKET VALUES: Original, Avg., High)

About the Red Pottery . . .

The Red Pottery was first introduced in 1992 but due to color problems was discontinued in 1993. After a short feature promotion later in 1993, a few pieces were reintroduced into the Regular Line in 1995. The balance of the pieces were brought back in 1996. Since this pottery is available again in the Regular Line, we do not currently consider it a part of the Secondary Market. A complete listing of all the pottery can be found in the Collector's Checklist to help inventory your entire collection.

Roseville Embossing

A. Roseville Bowls

Form No:
Small: 30058
Medium: 30091
Large: 30023

B. Roseville Pie Plate

Form No: 30015
No.Sold:

Came with a box and a recipe for Grandma Bonnie's famous Apple Pie.

C. Roseville Pitchers

Form No:
Small: 30082
Large: 30031

Retired Baskets

Features:

Offered at one time through the Regular Line. Baskets are listed in alphabetical order. The years offered are noted in parenthesis. Unless otherwise noted, the Original price listed is from the first year the basket was offered.

Photo	Description		MARKET VALUES Avg.	High
A.	(82–88) Bread (Old)	11.95	**46**	**80**
B.	(79–94) Cake (1st/h)	15.95	**58**	**100**
C.	(94) Cake (Natural)	46.95	**63**	**105**
D.	(79–80) Canister Set	39.95	**—**	**80**
	5" Measuring, w/lid			
	7" Measuring, w/lid			
	9" Measuring, w/lid			
E.	(79–94) Corn	29.95	**140**	**275**
	with Protector	39.95	**140**	**275**
F.	(94) Cracker (Natural)	20.95	**35**	**40**
	Cradles:			
	(79–86) Cradle, Doll [pg.73]	25.95	**169**	**275**
	(79–86) Cradle, Large [pg.73]	39.95	**340**	**475**
G.	(79–83) Cradle, Medium	37.95	**—**	**—**
H.	(79–93) Cradle, Mini	9.95	**76**	**120**
	(79–80) Cradle, Small [np]	35.95	**—**	**—**
I.	(94) Darning (Natural)	30.95	**57**	**110**
	Easter Baskets: (Renamed to Chore Baskets in 1987)			
	(79–87) Easter, Baby (st/h) [np]	8.95	**50**	**60**
J.	(79–87) Easter, Baby (sw/h)	9.95	**56**	**70**
K.	(79–87) Easter, Large (st/h)	11.95	**71**	**80**
	(79–87) Easter, Large (sw/h) [np]	12.95	**80**	**84**
	(79–87) Easter, Med. (st/h) [np]	10.95	**73**	**95**
L.	(79–87) Easter, Med. (sw/h)	11.95	**66**	**70**

(Easter Baskets continued next page)

KEY:

[np] = Not Pictured

[pg.xx] = This item is also featured in another section. Go to the page noted for a photo.

A. 1982–88 "Old" Bread

15^{L} x 8^{W} x 2.25^{H}

Form No: 4600-OO
No. Sold:

Replaced by a deeper Bread basket in 1988.

E. 1979–94 Corn

17RD x 11.5^{H}

Form No: 14401
No. Sold:

Inverted bottom, two hand slots. Reintroduced through the Hostess Collection with two braided ears in 1995.

I. 1994 Natural Darning

10RD x 4^{H}

Form No: 15521
No. Sold:

Available from Feb. 1 through Aug. 31, 1994.

B. 1979–94 Cake

$12^L \times 12^W \times 6^H$

Form No: 11002
No. Sold:

1 st/h, included divider.

C. 1994 Natural Cake

$12^L \times 12^W \times 6^H$

Form No: 16144
No. Sold:

Available from Feb. 1 through Aug. 31, 1994. Divider sold with basket.

D. 1979–80 Canister Set

5", 7" & 9" Measuring

5" Measuring: $5^{RD} \times 4.5^H$
7" Measuring: $7^{RD} \times 6.5^H$
9" Measuring: $9^{RD} \times 8.5^H$

Only sold as a set. No handles, included lids.

F. 1994 Natural Cracker

$11.5^L \times 5^W \times 3^H$

Form No: 17198
No. Sold:

Available from Feb. 1 through Aug. 31, 1994.

G. 1979–83 Medium Cradle

$28.5^L \times 17.75^W \times 9.75^H$

Form No: 2700–M
No. Sold:

Doll: $19^L \times 12^W \times 6^H$
Large: $30^L \times 20^W \times 10.5^H$
Small: $23.25^L \times 16.25^W \times 9.5^H$

H. 1979–93 Mini Cradle

$7^L \times 5^W \times 3.5^H$

Form No: 10715/700-K
No. Sold:

Had 2 wooden loops prior to 1984.

J. 1979–87 Baby Easter

$7^L \times 5^W \times 3.5^H$

Form No: 700-BO
No. Sold:

Also available with 1 st/h. (Form No. 700-AO)

K. 1979–87 Large Easter

$14^L \times 7.75^W \times 5.25^H$

Form No: 3600-AO
No. Sold:

Also available with 1 sw/h. (Form No. 3600-BO)

L. 1979–87 Medium Easter

$13^L \times 8^W \times 5^H$

Form No: 3500-BO
No. Sold:

Also available with 1 st/h. (Form No. 3500-AO)

Features:

All baskets prior to 1985 will have the older, darker stain and all baskets after 1987 will have the newer, lighter stain. The stain was changed sometime between 1986 and 1987.

MARKET VALUES

Photo	Description	Original	Avg.	High
	Easter Baskets: (con't)			
M.	(79–87) Easter, Small (st/h)	9.95	**49**	**60**
	(79–87) Easter, Small (sw/h)[np]	10.95	**60**	**75**
	Fruit Baskets – with Splint Hangers:			
	(79–80) Fruit, Lg. Hanging[np]	21.95	**100**	**140**
N.	(79–80) Fruit, Med. Hanging	15.95	**50**	**50**
O.	(79–80) Fruit, Small Hanging	11.95	**77**	**125**
	(79–80) Fruit, Tall Hanging[np]	18.95	**—**	**—**
P.	(79–95) Fruit, Tall	15.95	**68**	**110**
	Gathering Baskets:			
Q.	(83–93) Gathering, Lg. (1st/h)	26.95	**84**	**100**
R.	(79–94) Gathering, Lg. (2sw/h)	19.95	**76**	**120**
	(80–93) Gathering, Med.(1st/h)	41.95	**77**	**120**
S.	(86–93) Gathering, Sm. (1st/h)	22.95	**74**	**80**
	(79–86) Hamper, Lg. [pg.72]	59.95	**211**	**290**
	(79–86) Hamper, Sm./Med.[np]	31.95	**140**	**175**
T.	*Hanging Baskets – with Rawhide Hangers:*			
	(80–86) 5" Square bottom	14.95	**79**	**95**
	(80–86) 7" Square bottom	15.95	**70**	**85**
	(80–86) 9" Square bottom	22.95	**40**	**40**
	(80–86) 11" Square bottom	29.95	**40**	**40**
	(80–86) 13" Square bottom	35.95	**40**	**40**
U.	(79–86) Woven bottom	14.95	**85**	**100**
	Inverted Waste:			
	(79–84) Lg. Round (no/h)[np]	26.95	**85**	**110**
	(79–84) Lg. Round (1sw/h)[pg.63]	28.95	**114**	**120**
	(79–84) Sm. Round (no/h)[np]	21.95	**90**	**100**
V.	(79–84) Sm. Round (1sw/h)	23.95	**—**	**—**
W.	(94) Key, Tall (Natural)	31.95	**42**	**50**
	Laundry:			
	(79–86) Laundry, Large [pg.73]	34.95	**182**	**250**
X.	(79–83) Laundry, Medium	31.95	**—**	**—**

KEY:
[pg.xx] = This item is also featured in another section. Go to the page noted for a photo.

M. 1979–87 Small Easter

10L x 6W x 4H

Form No: 3400-AO
No. Sold:

Also available with 1 sw/h. (Form No. 3400-BO).

Q. 1983–93 Large Gathering

19L x 12W x 6H

Form No: 12505/12500-A
No. Sold:

Medium: 18L x 11W x 4.5H
12408

All Gathering baskets with 1st/h are currently retired.

U. 1979–86 Woven bottom

8.25RD x 7.75H

Form No: 3700-PO
No. Sold:

1979–80
N. Hanging Md. Fruit

8RD x 6.5^{H}

Form No: 3100-P
No. Sold:

Large: 13RD x 8.5^{H}
3200-P

1979–80
O. Hanging Sm. Fruit

6.5^{RD} x 5^{H}

Form No: 3000-P
No. Sold:

Tall: 8RD x 9^{H}
3300-P

1979–95
P. Tall Fruit

8RD x 9^{H}

Form No: 13307/13300-BO
No. Sold:

Inverted Bottom

1979–94
R. Large Gathering

19^{L} x 12^{W} x 6^{H}

Form No: 12513/12500-C
No. Sold:

This basket was brought back into the regular line through the Hostess Collection in 1996.

1986–93
S. Small Gathering

14^{L} x 9^{W} x 4.5^{H}

Form No: 12301/12300-AO
No. Sold:

Only the Small Gathering with 1 st/h has been retired. This basket with 2 sw/h is still available.

1980–86
T. Hanging Baskets

Dimensions:

5" :	5RD x 4.5^{H}
7" :	7RD x 6.5^{H}
9" :	9RD x 8.5^{H}
11":	11RD x 10.5^{H}
13":	13RD x 12.5^{H}

1979–84
V. Small Inverted

12.5^{RD} x 13.5^{H}

Form No: 1900-B
No. Sold:

Large: 14RD x 16^{H}
2000-O/B

Both available with 1 sw/h or without a handle.

1994 Natural
W. Tall Key

9.5^{L} x 5^{W} x 9.5^{H}

Form No: 14630
No. Sold:

Available from Feb. 1 through Aug. 31, 1994.

1979–83
X. Medium Laundry

28.5^{L} x 17.75^{W} x 9.75^{H}

Form No: 2700-O
No. Sold:

Large: 30^{L} x 20^{W}x 10.5^{H}
2800-OO

RETIRED BASKETS

Features:

From 1980 – 1986, most Regular Line baskets could be "customized" with color accent weaving and trim. See the Basket Fun Facts on page 118 for more information.

Photo	Description		Original	Avg.	High
				MARKET VALUES	
Y.	(79–95)	Magazine (1sw/h, legs)	21.95	**83**	**100**
Z.	(79–93)	Market, Large (1st/h)	19.95	**76**	**105**
A1	(79–93)	Market, Small (1st/h)	14.95	**67**	**125**
B1	(83–86)	Picnic, Family	98.95	**300**	**350**
		with Liner	135.90	**331**	**390**
C1	(79–84)	Picnic, Medium	26.95	**190**	**200**
		Planters:			
D1	(82–86)	Fern, Lg. (w/feet)	27.95	**120**	**180**
	(79–86)	Fern, Lg. (13" stand[np]	23.95	**121**	**200**
	(79–86)	Fern, Lg. (20" stand)[np]	26.95	**—**	**130**
E1	(82–86)	Fern, Sm. (w/feet)	21.95	**97**	**175**
	(79–86)	Fern, Sm. (13" stand)[np]	21.95	**115**	**130**
F1	(79–86)	Fern, Sm. (20" stand)	24.95	**138**	**150**
		Purse:			
G1	(94)	Purse, Kiddie(Natural)	28.95	**41**	**50**
H1	(82–86)	Purse, Med.(Split Lid)	24.95	**123**	**255**
I1	(79–89)	Purse, Tall	27.95	**117**	**160**
		Sewing:			
	(78–86)	Sewing, Round			
J1		with 13"stand	29.95	**197**	**300**
		without stand[pg.61]		**135**	**190**

[Sewing Baskets continued next page]

KEY:

[np] = Not Pictured

[pg.xx] = This item is also featured in another section. Go to the page noted for a photo.

Y. 1979–95 Magazine

16^L x 8^W x 11^H

Form No: 12122/12100-U

No. Sold:

1 sw/h, legs, no lid

C1 1979–84 Medium Picnic

15^L x 15^W x 7.5^H

Form No: 200-H

No. Sold:

G1 1994 Natural Kiddie Purse

7^L x 5^W x 3.5^H

Form No: 17019

No. Sold:

Available from Feb. 1 through Aug. 31, 1994.

Z. 1979–93 Large Market

$16^{L} \times 11^{W} \times 9^{H}$

Form No: 10626/600-AO
No. Sold:

This basket is still available with 2 sw/h. Only the 1 st/h option has been retired.

A^{1} 1979–93 Small Market

$15^{L} \times 9.5^{W} \times 5.5^{H}$

Form No: 10421/400-AO
No. Sold:

This basket is still available with 2 sw/h. Only the 1 st/h option has been retired.

B^{1} 1983–86 Family Picnic

$24^{L} \times 17^{W} \times 10^{H}$

Form No: 2600-HO
No. Sold:

Red Gingham liner also available. Most Family Picnic Baskets will look darker than this one.

D^{1} 1982–86 Large Fern

$13^{RD} \times 8.5^{H}$

Form No: 3200-RO
No. Sold:

E^{1} 1982–86 Small Fern

$8.5^{RD} \times 7.5^{H}$

Form No: 2900-RO
No. Sold:

These baskets are sometimes referred to as "Floor Planters" or planters with "feet". They are not Patio Planters. There was a Patio Planter featured in 1984 (see the Feature Section for photo).

F^{1} 1979–86 Small Fern

$8.5^{RD} \times 7.5^{H}$ (20" stand)

Form No: 2900-TO
No. Sold:

Available for either Large or Small Fern baskets, 13" or 20" stand. No feet on baskets. Not available without a stand.

H^{1} 1982–86 Medium Purse

$11^{L} \times 8^{W} \times 5.5^{H}$

Form No: 900-QO
No. Sold:

Split-lid option retired.

I^{1} 1979-89 Tall Purse

$9.5^{L} \times 5^{W} \times 9.5^{H}$

Form No: 1000-EO
No. Sold:

J^{1} 1978–86 Round Sewing

$13^{RD} \times 8.5^{H}$ (13" stand)

Form No: 3200-NO
No. Sold:

Split attached lid, 1 sw/h. Metal hinges changed to leather in 1979. Available with or without a stand.

Features:

All baskets listed were offered at one time through the Regular Line.

Photo		Description	MARKET VALUES Original	Avg.	High
K1	(78–83)	Sewing, Rectangular	26.95	**381**	**400**
L1	(79–94)	Umbrella	18.95	**95**	**150**
		with Protector		**124**	**160**
M1	(94)	Vegetable, Medium (Natural)	38.95	**40**	**65**
N1	(83-86)	Wine, Large	29.95	**91**	**120**
		Wrought Iron:			
	(96-97)	Herb Marker Gift Sets: [np]			
		Basil & Chives	19.95	—	—
		Parsley & Thyme	19.95	—	—

KEY: [np] = Not Pictured

K1 1978–83 Rectangular Sewing

$16^L \times 11^W \times 9^H$

Form No: 600-F
No. Sold:

Split attached lid, 2 sw/h. Had metal hinges in 1978, only.

L1 1979–94 Umbrella

$10^{RD} \times 17.5^H$

Form No: 11207/1200-OO
No. Sold:

M1 1994 Natural Med. Vegetable

$13^L \times 7.5^W \times 3^{FH} \times 8^{BH}$

Form No: 15113
No. Sold:

Available from Feb. 1 through Aug. 31, 1994.

N1 1983–86 Large Wine

$16^L \times 9^W \times 3.5^{FH} \times 9^{BH}$

Form No: 5200-CO
No. Sold:

Included dividers (wine rack)

Shades of Autumn®

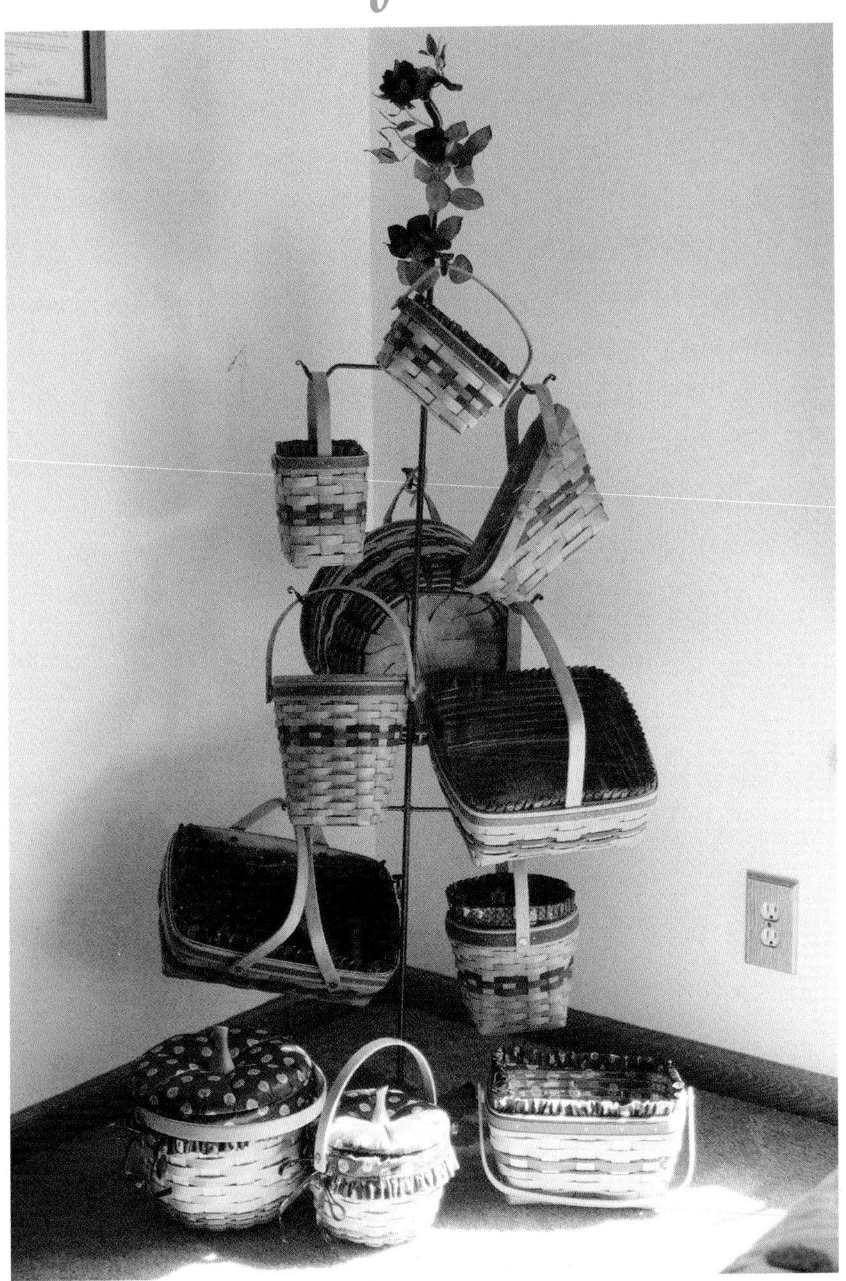

SHADES OF AUTUMN®

Features:

Rust trim. Green, Rust and Deep Blue weave.

MARKET VALUES

Photo		Description	Original	Avg.	High
A.	1990	Pie™	31.95	**118**	**150**
B.	1990	Small Vegetable™	35.95	**211**	**295**
C.	1991	Small Gathering™	36.95	**126**	**165**
		with **P**rotector	45.90	**128**	**200**
		with **L**iner	49.90	**128**	**200**
		Combo **(P/L)**	48.95	**146**	**245**
D.	1991	Acorn™	24.95	**124**	**160**
		with **P**rotector	28.90	**130**	**160**
		with **L**iner	35.90	**130**	**160**
		Combo **(P/L)**	35.95	**143**	**190**
E.	1992	Bittersweet™	24.95	**90**	**110**
		with **P**rotector	29.90	**90**	**125**
		with **L**iner	33.90	**90**	**125**
		Combo **(P/L)**	29.95	**95**	**130**
F.	1993	Harvest™	39.95	**95**	**130**
		with **P**rotector	45.90	**101**	**130**
		with **L**iner	52.90	**101**	**130**
		Combo **(P/L)**	49.95	**105**	**145**
F.	1993	Table runner	34.95	—	—
G.	1994	Recipe™	29.95	**88**	**125**
		with **P**rotector	34.90	**90**	**135**
		with **Lid**	42.90	—	—
		with Recipe Card Set	35.90	—	—
		Combo **(P/Lid/Cards)**	44.95	**135**	**145**
H.	1995	Basket of Plenty™	53.95	**109**	**135**
		with **P**rotector	61.90	**110**	**135**
		with **L**iner	73.90	**110**	**135**
		Combo **(P/L)**	69.95	**110**	**140**
		with Fabric Lid	78.90	—	—
		Full Set **(Combo/Lid)**	101.85	**115**	**170**
H.	1995	Fall Foliage Tie-On	6.95	**9**	**10**
I.	1996	Maple Leaf™	40.95	—	—
		with **P**rotector	46.90	—	—
		with **L**iner	56.90	—	—
		Combo **(P/L)**	54.95	**71**	**90**
		with **Lid**	60.90	—	—
		Full Set **(Combo/Lid)**	74.90	—	—
I.	1996	Maple Leaf™ Tie-On	6.95	**11**	**18**

A. 1990 Pie

12^L x 12^W x 4^H

Form No: 2200-AGUBS
No. Sold:

E. 1992 Bittersweet

5.5^L x 5.5^W x 6^H

Form No: 10804
No. Sold:

I. 1996 Maple Leaf

7RD x 6.5^H

Form No: 13935
Tie-On: 32999
No. Sold:

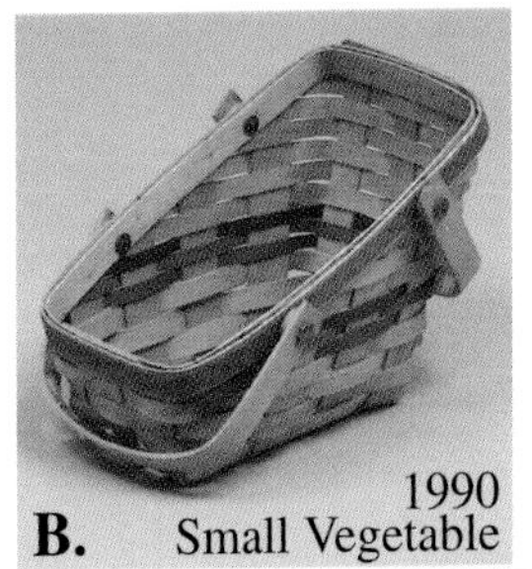

B. 1990 Small Vegetable

$10.5^{L} \times 6.5^{W} \times 3^{FH} \times 7^{BH}$

Form No: 5000-CGUBS
No. Sold:

Hostess Only

C. 1991 Small Gathering

$14^{L} \times 9^{W} \times 4.5^{H}$

Form No: 2300-CGUBS
No. Sold:

D. 1991 Acorn

$7^{L} \times 5^{W} \times 3.5^{H}$

Form No: 700-BGUBS
No. Sold:

F. 1993 Harvest

$7^{L} \times 4.75^{W} \times 7.75^{H}$

Form No: 14303
Tablerunner: 20150
No. Sold:

Liner is Autumn™. Reversible Table runner is Sunset™.

G. 1994 Recipe

$8^{L} \times 5.5^{W} \times 4.5^{FH} \times 6^{BH}$

Form No: 17400
No. Sold:

Basket included set of Recipe Cards.

H. 1995 Basket of Plenty

$12^{RD} \times 5.75^{H}$

Form No: 15563
Tie-On: 31755
No. Sold:

Tie-On and Fabric Lid sold separately.

About the Shades of Autumn Collection . . .

The selling season for this collection is usually during the month of July. In the past two years, this collection has been sold during the same selling campaign as the Horizon of Hope™.

This series continues to be one of the most popular series in the Secondary Market. Within the collection, the 1990 Small Vegetable seems to be the highest in demand. Due to its "Hostess Only" status, the number circulating in the market are expected to be much lower than the 1990 Pie, which was available to everyone.

• Basket Fun Facts •

Customizing Baskets

In past years, The Longaberger Company® allowed customers to "customize" their baskets. Customizing meant they were able to special order baskets with special features. Between 1977 and 1978, almost any combination could be ordered for a basket – stained, natural, with or without color weaving, lid no lid, handle, no handle, 1 handle, 2 handles, etc . . .. Because they were handmade and the orders were not as great as they are today, it was not hard to allow for this customizing policy.

In 1980, this policy was changed to only allow customers to choose between two special order options for an additional $5.00 charge: Natural or natural with color accent weave. The colors available for this option were:

BLUE

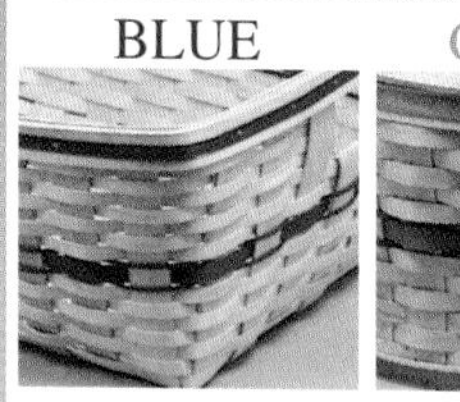

GREEN

BROWN

RED: Photo not available.

YELLOW:
Only available as a choice for a short time prior to 1980.

Exceptions . . .

Most baskets were included for this option, with the following exceptions:

Not available with Color Weaving; Could Only be Special Ordered in Natural:

Button	Cracker	Medium Vegetable
Bread	Small Vegetable	Wine

Available **Stained Only**; No Special Order Options:
All promotional baskets

Available **Only** Natural or Natural with Color; Could Not be ordered Stained:
1984 – 1989 : Large (Infant) Cradle, Large Laundry

Discontinued option . . .

The entire customizing option was discontinued for all Regular Line baskets in 1986. The option continued for the Large Cradle and Large Laundry until August 1989.

How does this option affect the Market Value . . .

How this option affects the value of the basket is hard to determine. Start by determining the value as if it were not customized. Some collectors who like the Naturals might be willing to pay more for the option, others do not. It is reasonable to consider the option worth at least $5.00 more valuable because that was the original cost for the option. However, the buyer's preference will ultimately determine if the basket is worth that or not.

Special Events

Features:
Baskets produced in honor of a special event.
Listed by year within its own category.
Commemorative Tag.

MARKET VALUES

Photo	Description	Original	Avg.	High
	Bob & Dolores Hope:			
A.	1989 Bob & Dolores Hope	N/A	**613**	**650**
B.	1990 Bob & Dolores Hope	N/A	**557**	**600**
C.	1991 Bob & Dolores Hope	N/A	**544**	**600**
D.	1992 Bob & Dolores Hope	N/A	**543**	**600**
E.	1993 Bob & Dolores Hope	N/A	**575**	**600**
F.	1994 Bob & Dolores Hope	N/A	**600**	**750**
G.	1995 Bob & Dolores Hope	N/A	**613**	**625**
	1996 Bob & Dolores Hope[np]	N/A	**575**	**575**
	[Series completed in 1996]			
	Inaugural:			
H.	1989 Inaugural™	19.89	**176**	**300**
I.	1993 Inaugural™	24.95	**80**	**115**
	with **P**rotector	28.90	**80**	**115**
	with **L**iner	34.90	**82**	**125**
	Combo **(P/L)**	34.95	**86**	**135**
J.	1997 Inaugural™	32.95	—	—
	with **P**rotector	36.90	—	—
	with **L**iner	44.90	—	—
	Combo **(P/L)**	42.95	**53**	**60**
J.	1997 Inaugural™ Tie-On	6.95	—	—
	Miscellaneous Events:			
K.	1992 Discovery™	19.92	**80**	**130**
	Combo **(L)**	29.87	**89**	**130**
L.	1996 Ohio Statehouse Opening	N/C	—	—

KEY: [np] = Not Pictured

A. 1989 Bob & Dolores Hope

$11^{L} \times 8^{W} \times 5.5^{H}$

Form No: 900-
No. Sold: ≈ 500

First Edition
Brown trim and center weave with blue shoestring weave.

E. 1993 Bob & Dolores Hope

$11^{L} \times 8^{W} \times 5.5^{H}$

Form No: 900-
No. Sold: ≈ 500

Fifth Edition
Blue trim with brown, blue, brown center weave. No shoestring weaving.

I. 1993 Inaugural

$5^{L} \times 5^{W} \times 4.5^{H}$

Form No: 11461
No. Sold:

In honor of President Clinton's Inauguration.

B. 1990 Bob & Dolores Hope

11L x 8W x 5.5H

Form No: 900-
No. Sold: ≈ 500

Second Edition
Blue trim and center weave with brown shoestring weave.

C. 1991 Bob & Dolores Hope

11L x 8W x 5.5H

Form No: 900-
No. Sold: ≈ 500

Third Edition
Blue trim with brown, blue, brown center weave. No shoe-string weaving.

D. 1992 Bob & Dolores Hope

11L x 8W x 5.5H

Form No: 900-
No. Sold: ≈ 500

Fourth Edition
Brown trim with blue, brown, blue center weave. No shoe-string weaving.

F. 1994 Bob & Dolores Hope

11L x 8W x 5.5H

Form No: 900-
No. Sold: ≈ 500

Sixth Edition
Blue trim and center weave. Brown shoe-string weave.

G. 1995 Bob & Dolores Hope

11L x 8W x 5.5H

Form No: 900-
No. Sold: ≈ 250

Seventh Edition
Blue trim and center weave. Brown shoe-string weave.

H. 1989 Inaugural

5RD x 4.5H

Form No: 3800-ABRST
No. Sold:

In honor of President Bush's Inauguration

J. 1997 Inaugural

5.5RD x 3.25H

Form No: 65323
Tie-On: 71609
No. Sold:

In honor of President Clinton's Inauguration.

K. 1992 Discovery

5.5RD x 3.5H

Form No: 5700-AO
No. Sold:

In honor of the Discovery of America. This basket was not made with double weaving. Protector not offered.

L. 1996 Statehouse

11L x 8W x 5.5H

Form No: 900-
No. Given: ≈ 400

Received at the Ohio Statehouse reopening in 1996.

• What's NEW •

Collectibles Database:

- Inventory ALL of your different collections with this one program.
- Keep track of years, signatures, condition, and much more.
- Print reports for insurance.
- Graph trends.
- Print *For Sale* or *Want Lists* for your spouse.

Unique Features:

- *Move Item Feature:* move over information from actual Collector Guides *directly* into your own collection.
- When time to update the information, you are able to purchase a renewal that will automatically update the old information with the new.
- *Find Feature* allows you to scan through the Guide to locate the baskets you have in your collection.
- *Collectible Details* appear as they do in the original Guides.

This database program is now available to help inventory your Longaberger Baskets®, Precious Moments®, Hallmark Ornaments, Cherished Teddies and much, much, MORE!

Call us TODAY for more information

1-800-VERIFY IT (1-800-837-4394)

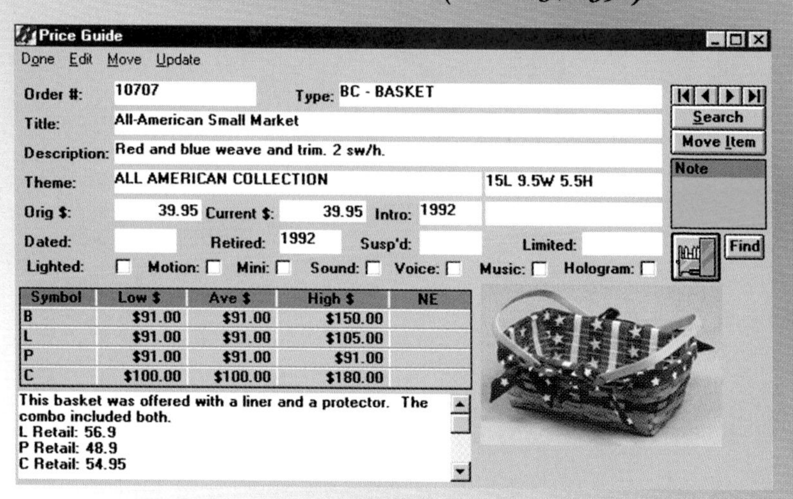

Features:

Red Shoestring Weaving.
Red Ticking Liners Starting in 1993.

Photo	Description	Original	Avg.	High
A.	1990 Sweetheart™	24.95	**98**	**125**
	Combo (**L**)	32.95	**109**	**145**
B.	1990 Getaway™	79.95	**144**	**180**
C.	1993 Sweetheart™	25.95	**74**	**160**
	with **P**rotector	28.90	**74**	**160**
	with **L**iner	35.90	**74**	**160**
	Combo (**P/L**)	29.95	**76**	**175**
C.	1993 Pewter Tie-On	8.95	**25**	**40**
D.	1993 Getaway™	119.95	**145**	**170**
	with **P**rotector	131.90	**145**	**190**
	with **L**iner	149.90	**145**	**190**
	Combo (**P/L**)	139.95	**145**	**190**
E.	1994 Be Mine™	27.95	**64**	**90**
	with **P**rotector	32.90	—	—
	with **L**iner	39.90	—	—
	Combo (**P/L**)	36.95	**67**	**100**
F.	1994 Forever Yours™	109.95	**138**	**160**
	with **P**rotector	123.90	**138**	**180**
	with **L**iner	139.90	**138**	**180**
	Combo (**P/L**)	139.95	**140**	**200**
E.	1994 Fabric Heart Tie-On	6.95	**13**	**18**
G.	1995 Sweet Sentiments™	28.95	**55**	**85**
	with **P**rotector	31.90	**60**	**85**
	with **L**iner	38.90	**60**	**85**
	Combo (**P/L**)	33.95	**65**	**125**
G.	1995 Small Heart Tie-On	5.95	**11**	**17**
H.	1995 Precious Treasures™	89.95	**168**	**200**
	with **P**rotector	100.90	—	—
	with **L**iner	116.90	—	—
	Combo (**P/L**)	99.95	**170**	**200**
	with **Lid**	119.95	—	—
H.	1995 Large Heart Tie-On	6.95	**15**	**20**
I.	1996 Bouquet™	34.95	—	—
	with **P**rotector	40.90	—	—
	with **L**iner	47.90	—	—
	Combo (**P/L**)	44.95	**60**	**65**
I.	1996 Bouquet™ Tie-On	6.95	—	—

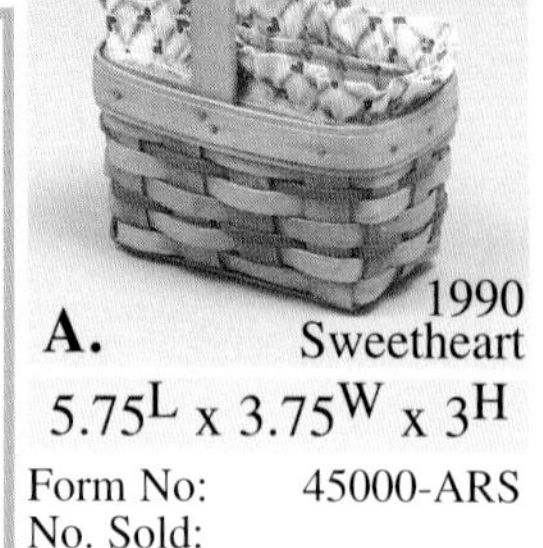

A. 1990 Sweetheart

5.75L x 3.75W x 3H

Form No: 45000-ARS
No. Sold:

E. 1994 Be Mine

8.5L x 5W x 3.5H

Form No: 18601
No. Sold:

I. 1996 Bouquet

6.5RD x 6.5H

Form No: 61221
Tie-On: 33596
No. Sold:

B. 1990 Getaway

17^L x 14^W x 11^H

Form No: 300-CRS
No. Sold:

Hostess Only

C. 1993 Sweetheart

5^L x 5^W x 2.5^H

Form No: 11347
Tie-On: 72036
No. Sold:

Tie-On sold separately.

D. 1993 Getaway

17^L x 14^W x 11^H

Form No: 10359
No. Sold:

Hostess Only

F. 1994 Forever Yours

20.5^L x 15^W x 10.5^H

Form No: 10367
Tie-On: 22659
No. Sold:

Hostess Only.
Tie-On sold separately.

G. 1995 Sweet Sentiments

4.25^L x 4.25^W x 3^H

Form No: 19046
Tie-On: 31780
No. Sold:

Tie-On sold separately.

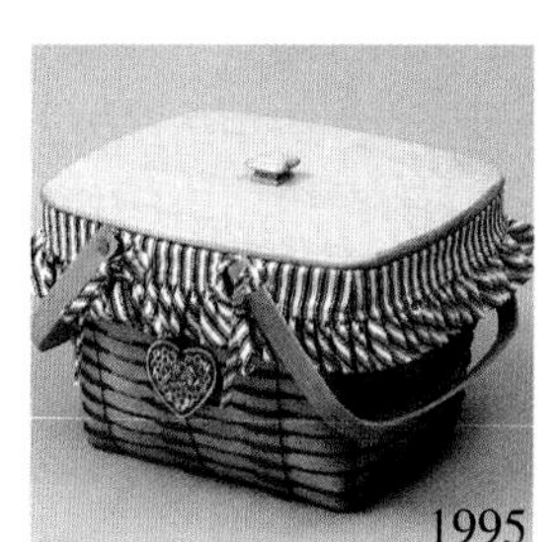

H. 1995 Precious Treasures

13.25^L x 11.25^W x 9^H

Form No: 10456
Tie-On: 31798
No. Sold:

Hostess Only.
Tie-On sold separately.

• *Collector Fun Facts* •

1996 research done by The Longaberger Company® revealed these interesting facts about their customers:

- The average customer purchases $310 in baskets a year.
- The most typical home decor preference was for "Country" and "Traditional".
- A very high percentage of their customers have computers and most have modems.

• Pottery Fun Facts •

The Longaberger Pottery® seems to take a back seat to the baskets. However, the Pottery has been a very important factor to The Company.

The history of Longaberger Pottery® started way back when the Longaberger Family first made Ware Baskets for local pottery companies to use when carrying the pottery from the kilns. 1990 was the first year for pottery in the regular line when they introduced the Roseville Pottery. The demand was high, but the production had some kinks. The production was moved to East Liverpool, Ohio in late 1991.

The current pottery dishes are available in Classic Blue™, Heritage Green™, Traditional Red™ and new Heirloom Ivory™. The Red Pottery was pulled from the line in 1993, but was reintroduced in full by 1996. Currently the only Longaberger Pottery® that is really active on the secondary market is the Roseville Pottery (see page 106).

Meadow Blossoms Pottery® was used as an incentive in 1985, but is just starting to show up in the Secondary Market. Available in thirteen different pieces, it could be earned in different groupings only by Consultants who sponsored recruits between April 1 and July 29, 1985 (see page 82).

Dishes, however, are not the only pottery items that have found success with The Company. Tie-ons have also performed very well on the primary <u>and</u> secondary market.

On the primary market, The Longaberger Company made $6-8 Million on Tie-Ons during 1995. In fact, the number one selling item for them in 1995 was the 1995 Mother's Day Tie-On, selling 90,515 pieces.

The Secondary Market also shows favor on Tie-Ons often doubling their value in just a year's time. The Collectors Club™ Membership Tie-On that was sent out *free* to members in May 1996 has mystified collectors in the market with its outstanding performance in less than a year (see page 33).

Tour Baskets™

TOUR BASKETS™

Features:

Previously called "Dresden Baskets". The only baskets that cannot be purchased through a Consultant. Available only in Dresden or Hartville. Brass Tag with date.

Photo	Description	Original	Avg.	High
		MARKET VALUES		
A.	*Dresden:*			
	1988 Tour™		—	—
	1989 Tour™		**58**	**70**
	1990 Tour™		**70**	**70**
	1991 Tour™		**78**	**85**
	1992 Dresden Tour™		**49**	**60**
	1993 Dresden Tour™	24.95	**53**	**60**
	with Protector	30.90	**58**	**60**
	1994 Dresden Tour™	29.95	**41**	**50**
	with Protector	35.90	**45**	**60**
	1995 Dresden Tour™	34.95	**65**	**70**
	with Protector	40.90	**70**	**95**
	1996 Dresden Tour™	34.95	—	—
	with Protector	40.90	—	—
	1997 Dresden Tour™	34.95	—	—
	with Protector	40.90	--	—
B.	*Dresden II:*			
	1996 Dresden Tour II™	29.95	**46**	**65**
	with Protector	33.90	—	—
	1997 Dresden Tour II™	29.95	—	—
	with Protector	33.90	—	—
C.	*Hartville:*			
	1995 Hartville Tour™	34.95	—	**60**
	with Protector	40.90	—	—
	1996 Hartville Tour™	34.95	—	—
	with Protector	40.90	—	—
	1997 Hartville Tour™	34.95	—	—
	with Protector	40.90	—	—
D.	*Hartville II:*			
	1996 Hartville Tour II™	29.95	—	—
	with Protector	33.90	—	—
	1997 Hartville Tour II™	29.95	—	—
	with Protector	33.90	—	—

A. Dresden Tour

8.75L x 4.75W x 6.5H

Form No: 5600-BO / 15601

Basket pictured is the actual first Tour Basket ever sold in Dresden in 1988.

B. Dresden Tour II

7L x 3.5W x 4.75H

Form No: 15814

This new form first appeared in Dresden & Hartville stores in Jan. 96.

C. Hartville Tour

8.75L x 4.75W x 6.5H

Form No: 15661

Same as the Dresden Tour, except different tag. First appeared in the Hartville factory store in 1995.

D. Hartville Tour II

7L x 3.5W x 4.75H

Form No: 15814

Traditions Collection™

Woven to reflect
Longaberger values . . .

g e n e r o s i t y
h o p e
c o m m i t m e n t

Features:
Heritage Green™ Weave and Trim.
Series introduced in 1995.
Commemorative Brass Tag.

MARKET VALUES

Photo	Description	Original	Avg.	High
A.	1995 Family™	89.95	**154**	**260**
	Combo **(P)**	95.95	**164**	**285**
	with **L**iner (1996)	119.90	—	—
	Full Set **(Combo/L)**	125.90	**215**	**285**
B.	1996 Community™	84.95	**125**	**170**
	with **P**rotector	93.95	**130**	**200**
	with **Liner**	114.90	**130**	**200**
	Combo **(P/L)**	109.95	**140**	**225**
	with **Div**ider	92.90	—	—
	Full Set **(Combo/Div)**	117.90	—	—
C.	1997 Fellowship™	69.95	—	—
	with **P**rotector	81.90	—	—
	with **L**iner	92.90	—	—
	Combo **(P/L)**	89.95	—	—
	with **Lid**	94.90	—	—
	with **Grip**per	97.90	—	—
	Full Set: **(Combo/Lid/Grip)**	129.95	—	—

A. 1995 Family
$15.25^{L} \times 11^{W} \times 7.75^{H}$
Form No: 19101
No. Sold:

3/8" Weaving. Liner added in 1996, not originally available.

B. 1996 Community
$14.75^{L} \times 13.5^{W} \times 6.25^{H}$
Form No: 19119
No. Sold:

Divider sold separately.

C. 1997 Fellowship
$12.5^{L} \times 6.5^{W} \times 7.75^{H}$
Form No: 15920
No. Sold:

Handle Gripper not shown.

Wood Products

WOOD PRODUCTS

Features:
Decorative handcrafted Wood Products. Years listed in parenthesis are the years the items were available.

Photo	Description	Original	Avg.	High
	Cupboards:			
A.	(80) 2-Door (Pine)		**350**	**450**
B.	(84–85) 1-Door (Maple)	119.95	**350**	**400**
C.	(84–85) 2-Door (Oak)	189.95	**475**	**500**
D.	(85–86) 1-Door (bottom shelf)	139.95	**392**	**450**
	Paddles:			
	Butter Paddles:			
	(83–85) 28^L x 4.5^W [np]	14.95	**32**	**45**
E.	(85–94) 28^L x 6.25^W	16.95	**—**	**—**
F.	**Stencil-Cut Paddles:**			
	(87–88) Heart™	14.95	**35**	**50**
	(87–88) Goose™	14.95	**28**	**40**
	(87–88) Gingerbread Man™	14.95	**43**	**55**
	Wall Hangings:			
	Rectangular, with shelf:			
G.	(79–84) 10^L x 14^H	16.95	**100**	**110**
H.	(85–86) 12^L x 16^H	39.95	**145**	**155**
	(79–80) 12^L x 24^H [np]	21.95	**150**	**180**
	Square, with shelf:			
I.	(79–80) Square, 20”	26.95	**168**	**180**
J.	(79–80) Square, 10”	12.95	**75**	**75**
	Triangle, with shelf:			
	(79–80) Triangle, 12^L x 10^H [np]	15.95	**130**	**180**
K.	(79–80) Triangle, 24^L x 21^H	23.95	**95**	**125**

KEY: [np] = Not Pictured

A. 1980 Pine Cupboard

15.5^L x 5^W x 32.75^H

Form No: unknown
No. Sold:

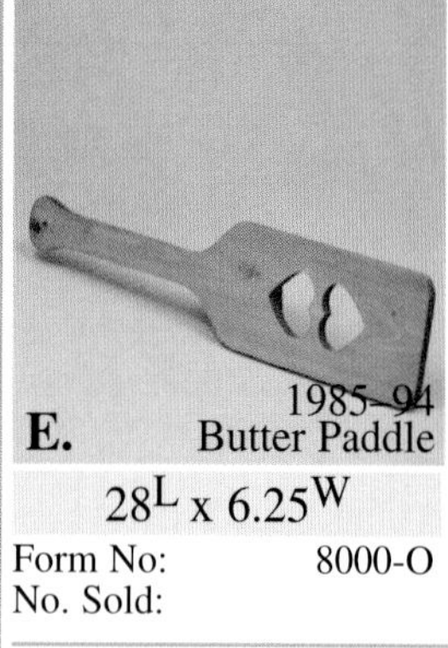

E. 1985–94 Butter Paddle

28^L x 6.25^W

Form No: 8000-O
No. Sold:

1983–85 Butter Paddle
28L x 4.5W 8010-O

I. 1979–80 Square

20^L x 20^H

Form No: 7701-O
No. Sold:

B. 1984–85 Maple Cupboard

27.5^{L} x 13^{W} x 5.25^{H}

Form No: 8101-OO
No. Sold:

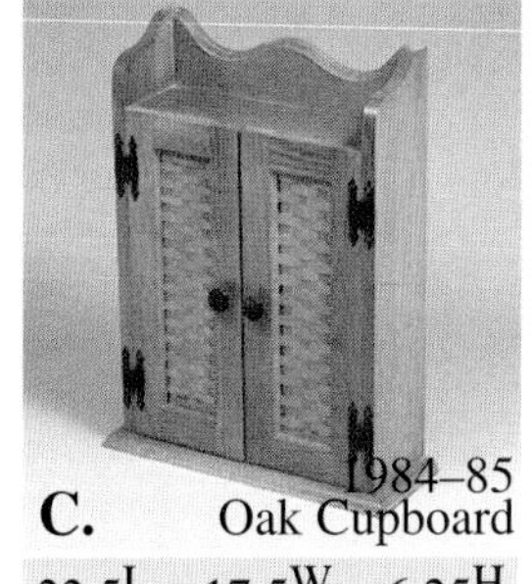

C. 1984–85 Oak Cupboard

22.5^{L} x 17.5^{W} x 6.25^{H}

Form No: 8100-O
No. Sold:

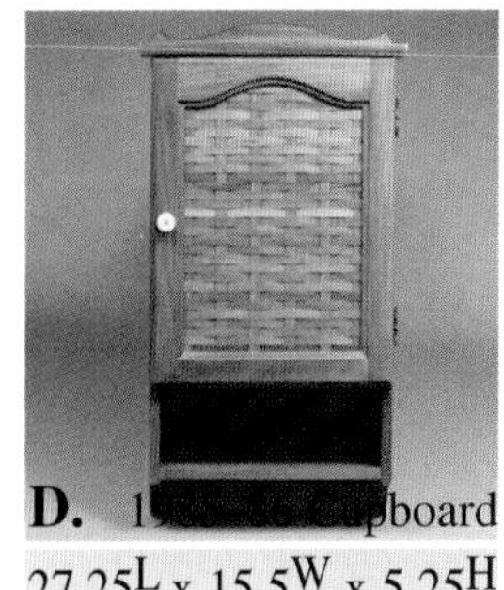

D. 1[illegible] [illegible]pboard

27.25^{L} x 15.5^{W} x 5.25^{H}

Form No: 8100-OO
No. Sold:

Also featured in 1988

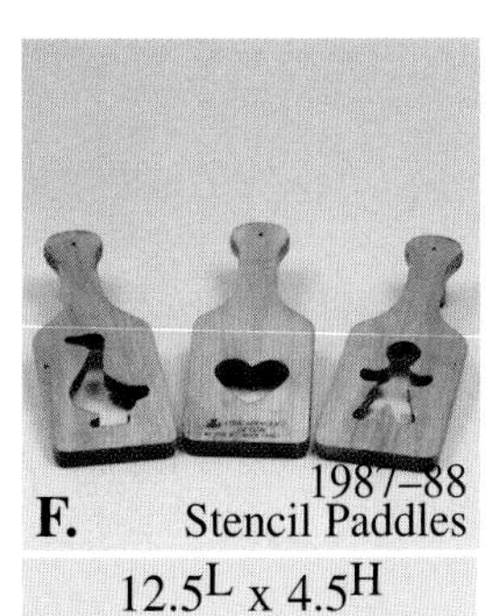

F. 1987–88 Stencil Paddles

12.5^{L} x 4.5^{H}

Form No:

Heart	8020-OO
Goose	8030-OO
Gingerbread	8040-OO

G. 1979–84 Rectangular

10^{L} x 14^{H}

Form No: 7800-OO
No. Sold:

12^{L} x 24^{W} 7801-O
Same style as the one above, only smaller.

H. 1985–86 Rectangular

12^{L} x 16^{H}

Form No: 7800-O
No. Sold:

J. 1979–80 Square

10^{L} x 10^{H}

Form No: 7700-O
No. Sold:

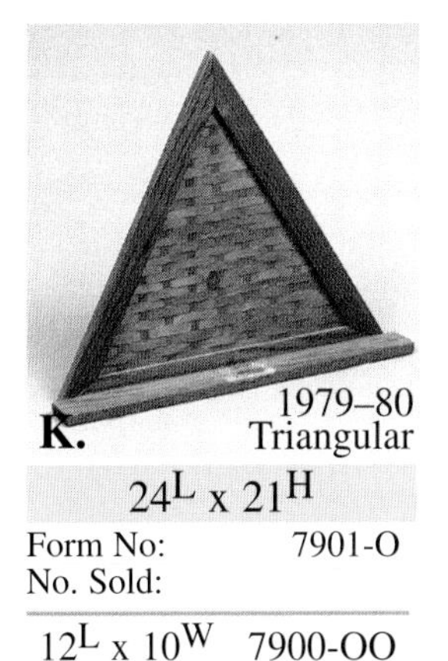

K. 1979–80 Triangular

24^{L} x 21^{H}

Form No: 7901-O
No. Sold:

12^{L} x 10^{W} 7900-OO
Same style as the one above, only smaller.

L. Wood Product Logo

Logo appears on all wood products starting in 1985. Unknown when the logo was changed to the current WoodCrafts® logo.

Features:

Decorative handcrafted Wood Products. Years listed in parenthesis are the years the items were available.

Photo	Description	Original	Avg.	High
	Wall Hangings: (con't)			
	Wall Brackets:			
L.	(79–85) Large	6.95	**33**	**33**
M.	(79–85) Small	5.95	**30**	**30**
	(85–86) Small [np]	12.95	—	—
	Miscellaneous Hangings:			
N.	(80) Framed Clock	39.95	**437**	**450**
	(80) Framed Mirror [np]	32.95	**383**	**400**
O.	(80) Picture Frame	29.95	—	**325**
P.	(80) Cathedral Mirror		**190**	**230**
Q.	(85–94) Peg Board	21.95	**37**	**50**
R.	(N/A) Nail Board		—	—
S.	(94-97) Wood Shelf		—	—
	Misc. Wood Crafts:			
T.	(79–82) Toilet Paper Holder	6.95	**48**	**50**
U.	(79–80) Towel Holder, 12"	8.95	**48**	**50**
	(79–80) Towel Holder, 18" [np]	10.95	—	**35**
	(79–80) Towel Holder, 21" [np]	11.95	—	—
	(79–80) Towel Holder, 24" [np]	12.95	—	—
V.	(80) Bread Box	N/A	**300**	**375**
W.	(80) Carpenter Box	N/A	**135**	**165**

KEY: [np] = Not Pictured

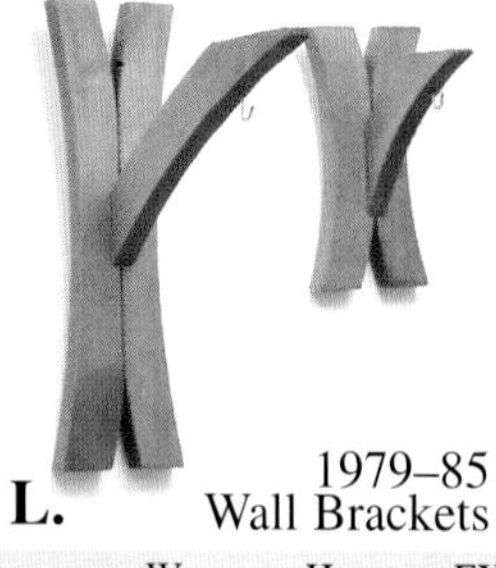

L. 1979–85 Wall Brackets

Lg: 4.5W x 13.5H x 11.5EXT
Sm: 4.5W x 8H x 6.5EXT

Form No:
Large: 8902-O
Small: 8900-O

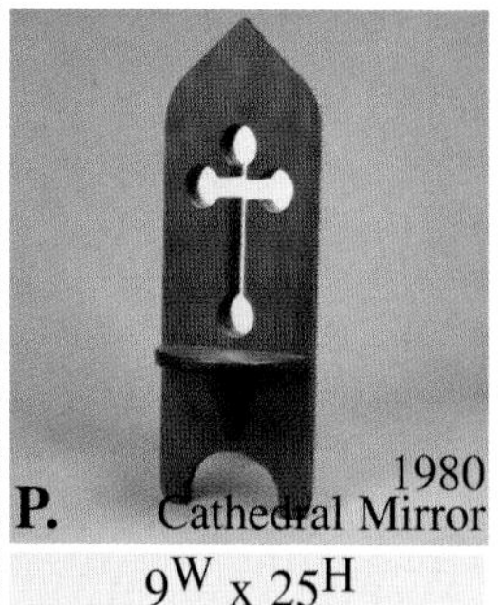

P. 1980 Cathedral Mirror

9W x 25H

Form No: unknown
No. Sold:

T. 1979–82 Toilet Paper Holder

8L x 3.5W

Form No: 8800-O
No. Sold:

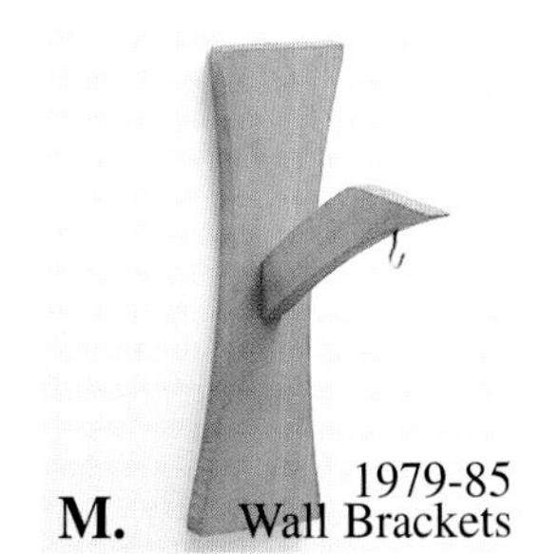

M. 1979-85 Wall Brackets

Both the "X" shaped brackets to the left and the "Hourglass" design above were offered from the company. When the change in design occurred is unknown. It was redesigned again in 1985, shaped like an upside down "L".

N. 1980 Framed Clock

20^L x 20^H

Form No: 7701-X

O. 1980 Picture Frame

20^L x 20^H

Form No: unknown

8 x 10 face. The Framed Mirror looks the same as this, except for a mirror in the opening.

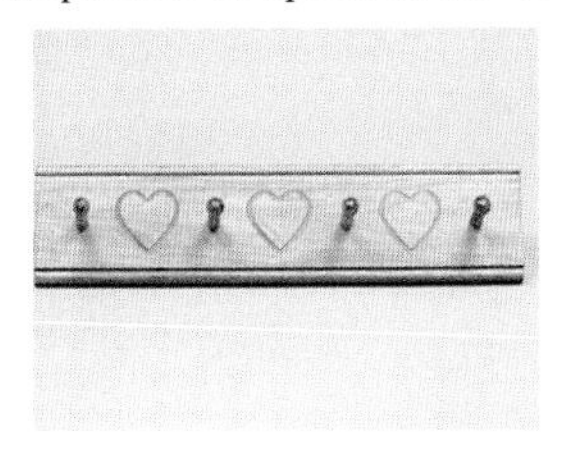

Q. 1985–94 Peg Board

23^L x 5^W x 5^H

Form No: 8801-O

Often promoted along with the Peg Baskets.

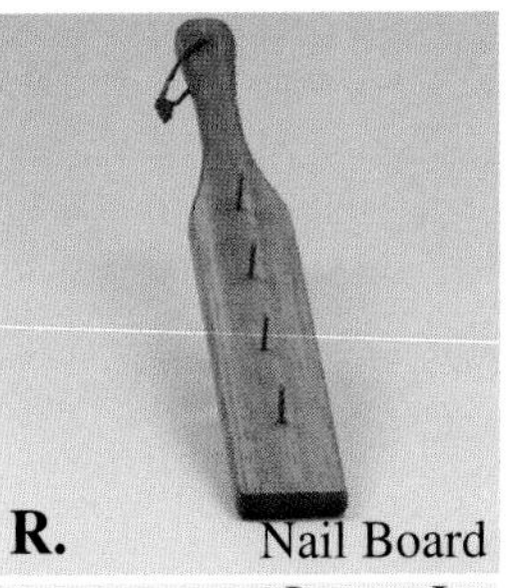

R. Nail Board

Approx. 16^L – 18^L

Form No: unknown
No. Sold:

S. 1994-97 Wood Shelf

32^L x 5.75^W x 5^H

Form No: 50601
No. Sold:

U. 1979–80 12" Towel Holder

15.5^L x 3.5^W

Form No: 8801-O

18" Holder: 19.5^L x 3.5^W 8802-O
21" Holder: 22.5^L x 3.5^W 8803-O
24" Holder: 25.5^L x 3.5^W 8804-O

V. 1980 Bread Box

18.5^L x 12.75^W x 13.5^H

Form No: unknown
No. Sold:

W. 1980 Carpenter Box

8^L x 6^W x 10^H

Form No: unknown
No. Sold:

Came with divider

Features:
Decorative handcrafted Wood Products.
Years listed in parenthesis are the years
the items were available.

Photo		Description	Original	Avg.	High
		Miscellaneous Wood Crafts (con't)			
X.	(80)	Cookbook Nook	N/A	**172**	**210**
Y.	(83–86)	Lids for Measuring Baskets:			
		5" Measuring	6.95	—	—
		7" Measuring	7.95	—	—
		9" Measuring	8.95	—	—
		11" Measuring	9.95	—	—
		13" Measuring	10.95	—	—
Z.	(80)	Cheese Board	N/A	—	—
A1	(81)	Wood Scoop	N/A	—	—

X. 1980 Cookbook Nook

13^W x 17^H

Form No: unknown
No. Sold:

Y. 1983–86 Measuring Lids

5", 7", 9", 11", 13"

5" Lid 8300-OO
7" Lid 8301-OO
9" Lid 8302-OO
11" Lid 8303-OO
13" Lid 8304-OO

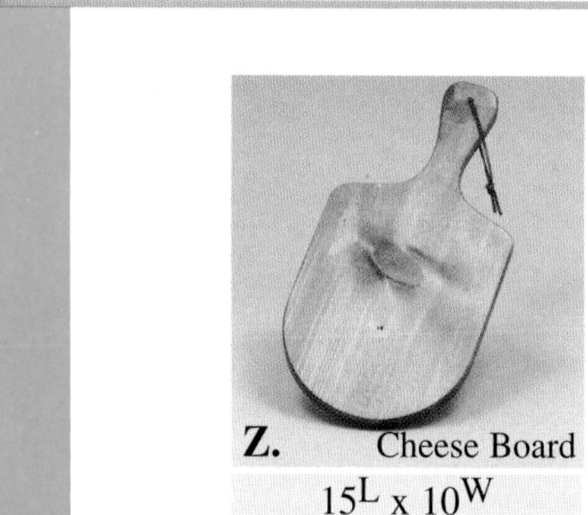

Z. Cheese Board

15^L x 10^W

Form No: unknown
No. Sold:

Dates unknown

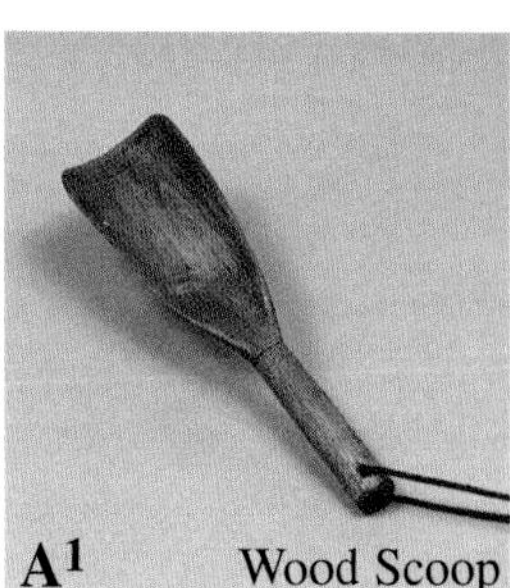

A1 Wood Scoop

Dimensions – N/A

Form No: unknown
No. Sold:

"Quick Find" Index

How To Use:

This quick-reference index was designed to help collectors easily find information concerning their baskets.

The *"Quick Find"* Index has been divided into six columns; **Basket, Collections (Year), Original Price, Market Value, Page in Guide, Form No., and Other Baskets Using Same Form**. Across the top of the right-hand page is also a quick index of which baskets are listed on that page of the index.

Basket

Each basket is listed alphabetically by name, not by collection. For example, the *J.W. Corn®* basket is found under *'C'* for *Corn*, not *"J"* for the *J.W. Collection®*. If you want to see the baskets by collection, the front part of the Guide is what you should use. Also listed in this column are the basket's dimensions.

Collections

This column lists all the different collections of which the basket has been a part. The number in parenthesis represents the year(s) that the basket was available. The letter 'P' in this parenthesis stands for 'Present' and means that the item is still available directly from the Company.

Original Price

The price that the basket originally sold for is listed in this column. The letter beside the value will tell the collector what the value is representing: **C** (Combo), **B** (basket only), **L** (basket sold with liner), or **P** (basket sold with protector).

Market Price

This year, both the ***Average and the High Market Values*** are listed in this column. In addition, if a collection has ** listed, this indicates that the basket may have several different market values, usually dependent on the year it was produced. When this notation is used, you will need to go to its location in the Guide or Checklist to find its value. If this column has been left blank or has dashed, a market value has not been determined.

Page in Guide

Refer to the listed page number or reference in order to obtain additional in formation on the basket or to find a picture of the basket. If 'checklist' is noted, this item is still available directly in the Regular Line and can only be found in the checklist. If the page number is green in color, a picture is not featured in the Guide.

Form No./Other Baskets U sing Same Form

Listed is the basket's form number(s) and then a compilation of the different baskets made with this same form and the same dimensions. This information is very useful when trying to identify what basket you have or when looking for an accessory to fit a discontinued basket.

Disclaimer

Basket	Collection(Year)	Original Price	Market Values*	
Acorn 7^L x 5^W x 3.5^H	Shades of Autumn(91)	35.95	**143**	**190 C**
Address 8.25^L x 6.25^W x 3.75^H	Father's Day(96)	34.95	**63**	**90 C**
Advisor Recognition 14^L x 9^W x 4.5^H	Incentive(86)	N/A	—	**95 B**
All-Star Trio 5.75^L x 3.75^W x 3^H	Feature(93)	29.95	**62**	**110 C**
Ambrosia 5.5^L x 4^W x 4^H	Employee Christmas(95)	N/A	**87**	**95 B**
	Booking(92-96)	22.95	**46**	**60 C**
American Beauty 13.5^L x 8.25^W x 5.25^H	Incentive(97)	N/A	—	—
Apple see **Large Fruit** 13RD x 8.5^H	J.W. Collection(85)	45.95	**609**	**800 B**
Associate Producer 5.5^{RD} x 2.5^H	Incentive(96)	N/A	—	—
Bakery 14.5^L x 7.5^W x 3.75^H	Heartland(90-P)	30.95		
	Feature(87)	22.95	**42**	**50 B**
Baking 14.5^L x 7.5^W x 3.75^H	Crisco® (93)	45.95	**110**	**150 C**
Banker's Waste 12.5^{RD} x 13.5^H	J.W. Collection(89)	59.95	**276**	**400 B**
Basket O' Luck 5.5^{RD} x 3.75^H	Feature(90)	N/A	**110**	**140 B**

KEY: * Market Values listed are the AVG and the HIGH Market Values.
C = Combo, **P** = with Protector, **L** = with Liner, **(-P)** = to present

Page in Guide	Form No.	Other Baskets Using Same Form
page 116	700-BGUBS	Basket of Thanks, Mini Berry, Mini Chore, Mistletoe, Mini Cradle, Baby Easter, 91 Hostess Easter, 93 Small Easter, 94 Employee Christmas, Kiddie Purse, Star Team, Small Key, Tea, Patriot
page 54	12611	None
page 82	2300-	92 Bee, 90 Employee Christmas Small Gathering, Tray, Pantry
page 58	64408	89 Employee Birthday, Keepsake, Paint the Town, 90 Recruit, Shining Star, Rosemary, Sugar and Spice, 90 Sweetheart, Treasure Chest, 95 Horizon of Hope
page 50 page 24	10120 10120	None
page 90	unknown	94 Easter
page 92	3200-BT	Large Fruit, Planter (Large Fern), Sewing (Round)
page 88	unknown	None
checklist page 62	14711 4700-JO	Bread (new), Breakfast, Baking, Rose
page 40	14745	Bakery, Bread (new), Breakfast, Rose
page 92	1900-BBST	Master Employee, Waste (Small Round Inverted), Tree Trimming
page 58	17000-AGS	Laurel, Lily of the Valley, Pot of Gold

KEY: In green = Not pictured in the Guide.
HL = Heartland® Collection, **WT** = Woven Traditions®, **R** = Red, **G** = Green

Basket	Collection(Year)	Original Price	Market Values*	
Basket of Plenty 12RD x 5.75^{H}	Shades of Autumn(95)	69.95	**110**	**140 C**
Basket Of Thanks 7^{L} x 5^{W} x 3.5^{H}	Incentive(93)	N/A	**72**	**110 B**
Bayberry 9^{L} x 9^{W} x 4.5^{H}	Christmas(93)	49.95	**82**	**140 C**
Be Mine 8.5^{L} x 5^{W} x 3.5^{H}	Sweetheart(94)	36.95	**67**	**100 C**
Bed 11.5^{L} x 5^{W} x 3^{H}	Feature(89)	29.95	**89**	**110 L**
Bee, Large 1988 14^{L} x 7.75^{W} x 5.25^{H}	Bee(88)	N/A	**145**	**165 B**
Bee, Medium 1988 13^{L} x 8^{W} x 5^{H}	Bee(88)	N/A	—	—
Bee 1989 8.75^{L} x 4.75^{W} x 6.5^{H}	Bee(89)	N/A	**145**	**180 B**
Bee 1990 7RD x 6.5^{H}	Bee(90)	19.90	**85**	**95 B**
Bee 1991 8.5^{L} x 8.5^{W} x 5^{H}	Bee(91)	19.91	**81**	**120 B**
Bee 1992 14^{L} x 9^{W} x 4.5^{H}	Bee(92)	20.00	**89**	**110 B**
Bee 1993 13^{L} x 8^{W} x 5^{H}	Bee(93)	25.00	**115**	**150 C**

KEY: * Market Values listed are the AVG and the HIGH Market Values.
C = Combo, **P** = with Protector, **L** = with Liner, **(-P)** = to present

Page in Guide	Form No.	Other Baskets Using Same Form
page 116	15563	High Achiever, Quilting
page 63	700-	Acorn, Mini Berry, Mini Chore, Tea Mistletoe, Mini Cradle, Patriot, Baby Easter, 91 Hostess Easter, 93 Small Easter, 94 Employee Christmas, Kiddie Purse, Star Team, Small Key
page 30	11584/11592	None
page 124	18601	92 Regional Sponsored Award, Small Oval, 93 Sponsor (Large), 97 Small Easter, Rose Petal
page 64	4500-AO	Liberty, Cracker, Muffin, Herb, 96 Employee Christmas
page 20	3600-AO	Large Chore, 88 Large Easter
page 20	3500-AN	Medium Chore, 88 Medium Easter, 93 Bee
page 20	5600-BRST	Dresden, Tour, Hartville, Flag, 92 Employee Birthday, Junior, Sophomore and Senior Recognition
page 20	3900-AO	7" Hanging, 7" Measuring, Poinsettia, 92 Sponsor (Large), Maple Leaf, 7" Canister
page 20	1500-	Large Berry, 88-89 Sponsor, 96 Bee
page 20	12335	Advisor Recognition, Tray, Pantry 90 Employee Christmas, Small Gathering
page 20	13501	Medium Chore, 88 Medium Easter, 88 Bee

Basket	Collection(Year)	Original Price	Market Values*	
Bee **1994** 6.5^{L} x 6.5^{W} x 8^{H}	Bee(94)	25.00	**206**	**325 C**
Bee **1995** 10^{L} x 6^{W} x 4^{H}	Bee(95)	42.90	**190**	**275 C**
Bee **1996** 8.5^{L} x 8.5^{W} x 5^{H}	Bee(96)	42.90	**135**	**250 C**
Bee, Speaker **1988** 15^{L} x 10^{W} x 7.5^{H}	Incentive(88)	N/A	—	—
Bee, Speaker **1990** 16^{L} x 9^{W} x 6^{H}	Incentive(90)	N/A	—	—
Bee, Speaker **1991, 1993-P** 11^{L} x 8^{W} x 5.5^{H}	Incentive(91, 93-P)	N/A	**	**
Bell 6.5^{RD} x 7^{H}	Christmas(83)	22.95	**615**	**750 B**
Berry, Large	J.W. Collection(90)	53.90	**180**	**280 C**
	Regular Line(no/h)(79-P)	8.95		
	Regular Line (1sw/h)(79-P)	10.95		
	Woven Traditions(92)	30.95		
8.5^{L} x 8.5^{W} x 5^{H}	Feature (1st/h)(85, 88)	18.95	**40**	**60 B**
Berry, Medium	All-American(87)	19.95	**111**	**150 B**
	Regular Line(no/h)(79-P)	7.95		
	Regular Line (1sw/h)(79-P)	9.95		
	Feature (1st/h)(85, 88)	17.95	**35**	**45 B**
7.5^{L} x 7.5^{W} x 3.5^{H}	Feature (96)	36.43C	—	—
Berry, Mini (see Tea) 7^{L} x 5^{W} x 3.5^{H}				

KEY: * Market Values listed are the AVG and the HIGH Market Values.
C = Combo, **P** = with Protector, **L** = with Liner, **(-P)** = to present

Page in Guide	Form No.	Other Baskets Using Same Form
page 20	unknown	Large Peg, Medium Spoon
page 22	unknown	93 Large Easter, Small Easter, Gingerbread, $500 Million, 91 Reg. Sponsored Award, Small Chore
page 22	unknown	91 Bee, 88-89 Sponsor, Large Berry
page 84	500-	87 Employee Christmas, Heirloom Medium Market, 77-87 Tenth Anniversary
page 84	3700-AOS	Harvest, Original Easter, Senior Employee
page 84	900-	Bob and Dolores Hope, Boo Basket, 91 Customer Easter, Medium Purse, Red Pottery Thank You, Spring, 96 Statehouse
page 28	4901-OO	None
page 92	1500-BBST	91 Bee, 88-89 Sponsor, 96 Bee
checklist	11509	
checklist	1428	
checklist	11533/1500-OO	
page 62	1500-AO	
page 14	1400-ABRS	95 Regional Sponsored
checklist	11410	
checklist	11428	
page 62	1400-AO	
page 60	16241/25/33	
checklist		Renamed Tea as of May 1, 1991

KEY: In green = Not pictured in the Guide.
HL = Heartland® Collection, **WT** = Woven Traditions®, **R** = Red, **G** = Green

Basket	Collection(Year)	Original Price	Market Values*	
Berry, Small	Regular Line(no/h)(79-P)	6.95		
	Regular Line(1sw/h)(79-P)	8.95		
6.5L x 6.5W x 3H	Feature(1st/h)(85, 88)	16.95	33	45 B
Best Supporting Role 8.5RD x 4H	Incentive (96)	N/A	105	150 B
Bittersweet 5.5L x 5.5W x 6H	Shades of Autumn(92)	29.95	95	130 C
Bob and Dolores Hope 11L x 8W x 5.5H	Special Events(89-96)	N/A	**	**
Boo 11L x 8W x 5.5H	Feature(94)	44.95	90	130 C
Bouquet 6.5RD x 6.5H	Sweetheart (96)	44.95	60	65 C
Branch Basket 15.75L x 6.5W x 11H	Incentive(88-P)	N/A	300	312 B
Branch Bouquet 10.5L x 6W x 4H	Incentive(97)	N/A	—	—
Bread (new)	Regular Line(88-P)	20.95		
	Woven Traditions(92-P)	36.95		
14.5L x 7.5W x 3.75H	Incentive(86)	N/A	145	175 B
Bread (old) 15L x 8W x 2.25H	Retired(82-88)	11.95	46	80 B
Bread & Milk	Feature(81)	unknown	675	750 B
16L x 8W x 11H	J.W. Collection(87)	43.95	425	550 B
Breakfast 14.5L x 7.5W x 3.75H	Feature(89)	37.95	87	110 B
Business Card 4.75L x 3.75W x 2.25H	Father's Day(94)	34.85	90	165 C

KEY: * Market Values listed are the AVG and the HIGH Market Values.
C = Combo, **P** = with Protector, **L** = with Liner, **(-P)** = to present

Page in Guide	Form No.	Other Baskets Using Same Form
checklist checklist page 62	11304 11312 1300-AO	Spare Change
page 88	unknown	Mother's Day 95
page 116	10804	Carry Along, Medium Peg, Small Spoon, 96 Sponsor, Shaker Peg
page 88	900-	91-P Bee Speaker, Boo Basket, 91 Customer Easter, Medium Purse, Red Pottery Thank You, Spring, 96 Statehouse
page 43	10987	91-P Bee Speaker, Bob and Dolores Hope, 91 Customer Easter, Medium Purse, Red Pottery Thank You, Spring, 96 Statehouse
page 124	61221	Lilac
page 84	unknown	Director Basket, Regional Basket
page 84	unknown	None
checklist checklist, WT page 82	14702/4700-OO 14737 4700-AO	Bakery, Breakfast, Crisco Baking, Rose
page 108	4600-OO	Holly, Garden
page 60 page 92	2100- 2100-ABT	Magazine
page 64	4700-AO	Bakery, Bread (new), Crisco Baking, Rose
page 54	17477	Star Bound

KEY: In green = Not pictured in the Guide.
HL = Heartland® Collection, **WT** = Woven Traditions®, **R** = Red, **G** = Green

Basket	Collection(Year)	Original Price	Market Values*	
Button	Employee Christmas(93)	N/A	**90**	**160 B**
	Booking (xx-84)	6.43 B	—	—
	Heartland(94)	22.95		
7RD x 3^{H}	Regular Line(84-P)	24.95		
Cake	All-American(88)	39.95	**127**	**180 B**
	Employee Christmas(88)	N/A	**143**	**180 B**
	J.W. Collection(92)	69.95	**175**	**250 C**
	Regular Line (2sw/h)(85-P)	26.95		
	Retired (1st/h)(79-94)	15.95	**58**	**100 B**
	Retired (Natrl)(94)	46.95	**68**	**105 B**
12^{L} x 12^{W} x 6^{H}	Woven Traditions(96)	59.95		
Candle	All-American(94)	42.95	**70**	**85 C**
	Booking(84-90)	N/A	**65**	**100 B**
	Christmas(81)	14.95	**600**	**850 B**
9^{L} x 5^{W} x 5^{H}	Employee Christmas(89)	N/A	**125**	**150 B**
Candy Cane 5^{L} x 5^{W} x 4.5^{H}	Christmas(86)	26.95	**180**	**280 B**
Canister Set Set of 3 Baskets	Retired (79-80)	39.95	—	**80 set**
Carry-Along 5.5^{L} x 5.5^{W} x 6^{H}	All-American(95)	44.95	**67**	**100 C**
Chives 4^{L} x 4^{W} x 4^{H}	Regular Line (96)	25.95		
Chore, Large 14^{L} x 7.75^{W} x 5.25^{H}	Feature(86)	23.95	**51**	**60 B**
Chore, Medium	Easter(87)	28.95	**91**	**115 B**
	Feature(86)	18.95	**53**	**55 B**
	Heartland(88-P)	36.95		
	Regular Line(86-P)	40.95		
13^{L} x 8^{W} x 5^{H}				
Chore, Mini	Heartland(89-P)	19.95		
	Mother's Day(89)	29.95	**100**	**150 B**
7^{L} x 5^{W} x 3.5^{H}				

KEY: * Market Values listed are the AVG and the HIGH Market Values.
C = Combo, **P** = with Protector, **L** = with Liner, **(-P)** = to present

Page in Guide	Form No.	Other Baskets Using Same Form
page 50	5400-	Stitching, Cookie, Show Star
page 24	5400-JO	
checklist, HL	5400-CO	
checklist	15423	
page 14	100-GBRS	Crisco Pie, Oak Lid Picnic, Small Picnic, 88 Employee Christmas
page 50	100-	
page 92	100-CBST	
checklist	11011/100-GO	
page 108	11002/100-A	
page 108	16144	
checklist, WT	11011	
page 16	11134	90 Sponsor, Medium Key, 96 Perfect Attendance, 89 Employee Christmas, 97 Renewal
page 24	1100-AO	
page 28	1100-	
page 50	1100-	
page 28	14000-ART/AGT	93 Inaugural, Violet, Small Peg, 96 Recruit, Tea Spoon
page 108	4700/4800/4900-O	See Measuring (5", 7" and 9")
page 16	14656	Bittersweet, Medium Peg, Small Spoon, 96 Sponsor, Shaker Peg
checklist, Booking	15211	None
page 62	3600-CO	88 Bee, Large Easter
page 42	3500-CX	93 Bee, Medium Easter, 88 Bee
page 62	3500-CO	
checklist, HL	13528 /3500-CO	
checklist	13510 /3500-CO	
checklist, HL	10758 /700-ACS	Acorn, Basket of Thanks, Tea, Mini Berry, Mistletoe, Mini Cradle, Baby Easter, 91 Hostess Easter, 93 Small Easter, 94 Employee Christmas, Patriot, Kiddie Purse, Star Team, Small Key
page 100	700-APS	

KEY: In green = Not pictured in the Guide.
HL = Heartland® Collection, **WT** = Woven Traditions®, **R** = Red, **G** = Green

Basket	Collection(Year)	Original Price	Market Values*	
Chore, Small	Heartland (89-P)	22.95		
	Feature (86)	17.95	**55**	**60 B**
10^L x 6^W x 4^H				
Collectors Club Membership	Collectors Club (95-P)	103.90	**158**	**230 C**
9.5^L x 5^W x 9.5^H				
Collectors Club Renewal	Collectors Club (97-P)	59.85 C	—	—
9^L x 5^W x 5^H				
Community	Traditions (96)	109.95	**140**	**225 C**
14.75^L x 13.5^W x 6.25^H				
Cookie	Christmas (85)	33.95	**243**	**300 L**
7RD x 3^H				
Cookie, Crisco	Crisco® (92)	39.95	**135**	**170 C**
10RD x 4^H				
Corn	J.W. Collection (91)	103.90	**330**	**480 C**
	Regular Line (95-P)	139.95		
17RD x 11.5^H	Retired (79-94)	39.95	**140**	**275 P**
Coverlet	Incentive (88)	N/A	—	—
16^L x 16^W x 8^H				
Cracker	Employee Christmas (96)	N/A	—	—
	Regular Line (83-P)	9.95		
	Retired (Natrl) (94)	20.95	**35**	**40 B**
11.5^L x 5^W x 3^H	Woven Traditions (92-P)	26.95		
Cradle, Doll	Hostess (86-90)	44.95	**162**	**225 B**
19^L x 12^W x 6^H	Retired (79-86)	25.95	**169**	**275 B**
Cradle, Large (Infant)	Hostess (86-90)	109.95	**300**	**400 B**
	Retired (79-86)	39.95	**340**	**475 B**
30^L x 20^W x 10.5^H				
Cradle, Medium	Retired (79-83)	37.95	—	—
28.5^L x 17.75^W x 9.75^H				

KEY: * Market Values listed are the AVG and the HIGH Market Values.
C = Combo, **P** = with Protector, **L** = with Liner, **(-P)** = to present

Page in Guide	Form No.	Other Baskets Using Same Form
checklist, HL page 62	13404 3400-CO	93 Large Easter, 88 Small Easter, Gingerbread, 91 Regional Sponsored Award, 95 Bee, $500 Million
page 32	62839	91 Employee Christmas, MBA, Tall Purse, Two-Quart, Tall Key
page 32	105702	Candle, 89 Employee Christmas, 90 Sponsor, Medium Key, 96 Perfect Attendance
page 130	19119	None
page 28	5400-AR / G	Stitching, Button, 93 Employee Christmas
page 40	10081	Daisy, Darning, 89 Easter, 96 Regional Sponsored
page 92 checklist, Hostess page 108	4400-JBST 14443 14401 /4400-OO	None
page 80	unknown	None
page 50 checklist page 108 checklist, WT	4500- 14508 /4500-OO 17198 14532	Liberty, Bed, Muffin, Herb 96 Employee Christmas
page 72 page 108	2500-LO 2500-LO	Large Gathering
page 72 page 108	2800-M 2800-MO	Large Laundry
page 108	2700-M	Medium Laundry

KEY: In green = Not pictured in the Guide.
HL = Heartland® Collection, **WT** = Woven Traditions®, **R** = Red, **G** = Green

Basket	Collection (Year)	Original Price	Market Values*	
Cradle, Mini $7^L \times 5^W \times 3.5^H$	Retired (79-93)	9.95	**76**	**120 B**
Cradle, Small $24^L \times 17^W \times 10^H$	Retired (79-80)	35.95	—	—
Cranberry $8.5^L \times 8.5^W \times 7^H$	Christmas (95)	59.95	**90**	**110 C**
Daisy $10^{RD} \times 4^H$	Feature(Stained) (86, 87)	25.95	**68**	**95 B**
	Feature(Natrl) (86)	27.95	**63**	**70 B**
Darning $10^{RD} \times 4^H$	Heartland (96-P)	39.95		
	Regular Line (83-P)	15.95		
	Retired(Natrl) (94)	30.95	**57**	**110 B**
	Woven Traditions (94-P)	39.95		
Director Basket $15.75^L \times 6.5^W \times 11^H$	Incentive (88-P)	N/A	—	—
Discovery $5.5^{RD} \times 3.5^H$	Special Event (92)	29.87	**87**	**130**
Dresden Basket see **Tour** $8.75^L \times 4.75^W \times 6.5^H$			**	**
Dresden Basket II see **Tour II** $7^L \times 3.5^W \times 4.75^H$			**	**
Easter (1989) $10^{RD} \times 4^H$	Easter (89)	29.95	**	**
Easter (1992) $10.5^L \times 7.5^W \times 4.5^H$	Easter (92)	39.95	**70**	**90 C**
Easter (1994) $13.5^L \times 8.25^W \times 5.25^H$	Easter (94)	59.95	**70**	**100 C**

KEY: * Market Values listed are the AVG and the HIGH Market Values.
C = Combo, **P** = with Protector, **L** = with Liner, **(-P)** = to present

Page in Guide	Form No.	Other Baskets Using Same Form
page 108	10715/700-K	Acorn, Basket of Thanks, Tea, Mini Berry, Mini Chore, Mistletoe, Baby Easter, 91 Hostess Easter, 93 Small Easter, 94 Employee Christmas, Kiddie Purse, Star Team, Small Key, Patriot
page 108	2600-M	Small Laundry, Family Picnic
page 30	19500^{R} / 19518^{G}	None
page 62 page 62	5500-AO 5500-AN	Crisco Cookie, Darning, 89 Easter, 96 Regional Sponsored
checklist checklist page 108 checklist	15598 15504 /500-JO 15521 15539	Crisco Cookie, Daisy, 89 Easter 96 Regional Sponsored
page 84	unknown	Branch Basket, Regional Basket
page 120	5700-AO	None
page 92	100114/5600-	89 Bee, 92 Employee Birthday, Junior Recognition, Memory, Sophomore Recognition, Hartville, Tour, Flag
page 92	unknown	Tour II
page 42	5500-ABS/AO/APS	Crisco Cookie, Daisy, Darning 96 Regional Sponsored
page 44	34000-APVCNK	None
page 44	16934	None

KEY: In green = Not pictured in the Guide.
HL = Heartland® Collection, **WT** = Woven Traditions®, **R** = Red, **G** = Green

Basket	Collection(Year)	Original Price	Market Values*	
Easter (1995) 10.75L x 8.75W x 5.25H	Easter (95)	59.95	**83**	**90 C**
Easter (1996) 7.5L x 5W x 6H	Easter (96)	49.95	**63**	**100 C**
Easter, Baby 7L x 5W x 3.5H	Easter (88)	18.95	**70**	**95 B**
	Retired(1st/h) (79-87)	8.95	**50**	**60 B**
	Retired(1sw/h) (79-87)	9.95	**56**	**70 B**
Easter, Customer (1991) 11L x 8W x 5.5H	Easter (91)	26.95	**59**	**95 B**
Easter, Hostess (1991) 7L x 5W x 3.5H	Easter (91)	21.95	**59**	**80 B**
Easter, Large (1988) 14L x 7.75W x 5.25H	Easter (88)	32.95	**80**	**95 B**
	Retired(1st/h) (79-87)	11.95	**71**	**80 B**
	Retired(1sw/h) (79-87)	12.95	**80**	**84 B**
Easter, Large (1990) 9.5RD x 5H	Easter (90)	43.95	**76**	**100 B**
Easter, Large (1993) 10L x 6W x 4H	Easter (93)	38.95	**67**	**110 C**
Easter, Large (1997) 12L x 7W x 4.5H	Easter (97)	52.95 C	—	—
Easter, Medium (1988) 13L x 8W x 5H	Easter (88)	28.95	**76**	**85 B**
	Retired(1st/h) (79-87)	10.95	**73**	**95 B**
	Retired(1sw/h) (79-87)	11.95	**66**	**70 B**
Easter, Medium (1990) 8RD x 4.5H	Easter (90)	38.95	**74**	**100 B**

KEY: * Market Values listed are the AVG and the HIGH Market Values.
C = Combo, **P** = with Protector, **L** = with Liner, **(-P)** = to present

Page in Guide	Form No.	Other Baskets Using Same Form
page 44	18708	None
page 44	12912	None
page 42 page 108 page 108	700-AN 700-AO 700-BO	Acorn, Basket of Thanks, Tea, Mini Berry, Mini Chore, Mistletoe, Small Key, Mini Cradle, 91 Hostess Easter, 93 Small Easter, Kiddie Purse, Patriot 94 Employee Christmas, Star Team
page 44	900-ATMS/ATMN	91-P Bee Speaker, Bob & Dolores Hope, Boo, Medium Purse, Red Pottery Thank You, Spring, 96 Statehouse
page 44	700-ATMS/ATMN	Acorn, Basket of Thanks, Tea, Mini Berry, Mini Chore, Mistletoe, Mini Cradle, Baby Easter, 93 Small Easter, Patriot, 94 Employee Christmas, Kiddie Purse, Star Team, Small Key
page 42 page 108 page 108	3600-AN 3600-AO 3600-BO	88 Bee, Large Chore
page 42	41000-APVBS	Petunia
page 44	13439	Gingerbread, Small Chore, 88 Small Easter, 91 Regional Sponsored Award, 95 Bee, $500 Million
page 44	13447	Rose Garden
page 42 page 108 page 108	3500-AN 3500-AO 3500-BO	93 Bee, Medium Chore, 88 Bee
page 42	40000-APVBS	None

KEY: In green = Not pictured in the Guide.
HL = Heartland® Collection, **WT** = Woven Traditions®, **R** = Red, **G** = Green

Basket	Collection (Year)	Original Price	Market Values*	
Easter, Small (1988) $10^{L} \times 6^{W} \times 4^{H}$	Easter (88)	22.95	**67**	**90 B**
	Retired(1st/h) (79-87)	9.95	**49**	**60 B**
	Retired(1sw/h) (79-87)	10.95	**60**	**75 B**
Easter, Small (1993) $7^{L} \times 5^{W} \times 3.5^{H}$	Easter (93)	35.95	**63**	**105 C**
Easter, Small (1997) $8.5^{L} \times 5^{W} \times 3.5^{H}$	Easter (97)	29.95 C	—	—
Evergreen $15.5^{L} \times 15.5^{W} \times 12.25^{H}$	Holiday Hostess (95)	199.95	**185**	**250 C**
Everything's Coming Up Roses (small) see **Rose Bud**				
Everything's Coming Up Roses (medium) see **Rose Petal**				
Everything's Coming Up Roses (large) see **American Beauty**				
Family $15.25^{L} \times 11^{W} \times 7.75^{H}$	Traditions (95)	95.95	**164**	**285 C**
Fellowship $12.5^{L} \times 6.5^{W} \times 7.75^{H}$	Tradition (97)	89.95 C	—	—
$500 Million $10^{L} \times 6^{W} \times 4^{H}$	Incentive (97)	N/A	—	—
Flag $8.75^{L} \times 4.75^{W} \times 6.5^{H}$	Incentive (89)	N/A	—	—
Flower Pot Basket $17^{L} \times 7.5^{W} \times 4.75^{H}$	Regular Line (95-P)	47.95		

KEY: * Market Values listed are the AVG and the HIGH Market Values.
C = Combo, **P** = with Protector, **L** = with Liner, **(-P)** = to present

Page in Guide	Form No.	Other Baskets Using Same Form
page 42 page 110 page 110	3400-AN 3400-AO 3400-BO	Gingerbread, Small Chore, 93 Large Easter, 95 Bee, 91 Regional Sponsored Award, $500 Million
page 44	10774	Acorn, Basket of Thanks, Tea, Mini Berry, Mini Chore, Mistletoe, Mini Cradle, Baby Easter, Patriot, 91 Hostess Easter, 94 Employee Christmas, Kiddie Purse, Star Team, Small Key
page 44	63541	Be Mine, 93 Sponsor (All-Star), 92 Regional Sponsored Award, Small Oval, Rose Petal
page 70	19607R / 19615G	None
page 88	unknown	93 Recruit, 93 Sponsor (Small), Lavender, 94 Hostess Appreciation
page 88	unknown	Small Oval, Be Mine, 93 Sponsor (All-Star), 92 Regional Sponsored Award, 97 Small Easter
page 90	unknown	94 Easter
page 130	19101	None
page 130	15920	None
page 82	900-	Gingerbread, 95 Bee, 93 Large Easter, 88 Small Easter, 91 Regional Sponsor, Small Chore,
page 80	unknown	Tour, 89 Bee, 92 Employee Birthday, Junior Recognition, Memory, Sophomore Recognition, Hartville, Dresden
checklist	16306	None

KEY: In green = Not pictured in the Guide.
HL = Heartland® Collection, **WT** = Woven Traditions®, **R** = Red, **G** = Green

Basket	Collection(Year)	Original Price	Market Values*	
Flower Pot Basket, Small 14L x 6W x 3H	Regular Line (96-P)	34.95		
Forever Yours 20.5L x 15W x 10.5H	Sweetheart (94)	139.95	**140**	**200 C**
Forget-Me-Not 5RD x 4.5H	Booking(86-87)	N/A	**55**	**85 B**
Friendship 5.5L x 5.5W x 2.5H	Feature (89)	21.95	**55**	**75 B**
Fruit, Large (Apple)	Holiday Hostess (89)	49.95	**133**	**165 B**
	Incentive, Recruit (88)	N/A	**—**	**140 B**
	Incentive, N.Sales (93)	N/A	**	**
	Regular Line (79-P)	18.95		
13RD x 8.5H	Retired, hanging (79-80)	21.95	**100**	**140 B**
Fruit, Medium	Incentive, Recruit (88)	N/A		
	Incentive, N.Sales (93)	N/A	**	**
	Regular Line (79-P)	12.95		
8RD x 6.5H	Retired, hanging (79-80)	15.95	**50**	**50 B**
Fruit, Small	Incentive, Recruit (88)	N/A		
	Incentive, N.Sales (93)	N/A	**	**
	Regular Line (79-P)	9.95		
6.5RD x 5H	Retired, hanging (79-80)	11.95	**77**	**125 B**
Fruit, Tall	Retired, hanging (79-80)	18.95	—	—
8RD x 9H	Retired (79-95)	15.95	**68**	**110 B**
Garden	Feature (86)	32.90set	**83**	**110 B**
15L x 8W x 2.25H	Incentive (88)	N/A	**80**	**80 B**
Gathering, Large	Holiday Hostess (90)	65.95	**124**	**160 B**
	Incentive, N.Sponsor (93-P)	N/A	**	**
	Regular Line (96-P)	89.95		
	Retired(1st/h) (83-93)	26.95	**84**	**100 B**
19L x 12W x 6H	Retired(2sw/h) (79-94)	19.95	**76**	**120 B**

KEY: * Market Values listed are the AVG and the HIGH Market Values.
C = Combo, **P** = with Protector, **L** = with Liner, **(-P)** = to present

Page in Guide	Form No.	Other Baskets Using Same Form
checklist	18414	Personal Organizer
page 124	10367	Gift Giving
page 24	3800-AO	89 Inaugural, 88 Employee Birthday, 5" Hanging, 92 Sponsor (Small), 92 Employee Christmas, Resolution, 5" Measuring, 92 Recruit, 5" Canister
page 64	13100-JO	91 Employee Birthday, Ivy, 95 Hostess Appreciation
page 68 page 76 page 80 checklist page 110	3200-BGRS 3200-BO 3200- 13200/3200-BO 3200-P	Apple, Planter (Large Fern), Sewing (Round)
page 76 page 80 checklist page 110	3100-BO 3100- 13102/3100-BO 3100-P	None
page 76 page 80 checklist page 110	3000-BO 3000- 13005/3000-BO 3000-P	Perfect Attendance
page 110 page 81	3300-P 13307/3300-BO	None
page 62 page 82	4600-AO 4700-	Bread (old), Holly
page 68 page 78 checklist, Hostess page 110 page 110	2500-CGRS 2500- 12564 12505/2500-A 12513/2500-O	Doll Cradle

KEY: In green = Not pictured in the Guide.
HL = Heartland® Collection, **WT** = Woven Traditions®, **R** = Red, **G** = Green

Basket	Collection(Year)	Original Price	Market Values*	
Gathering, Medium	Feature (Natrl) (87)	41.95	—	—
	Holiday Hostess (89)	40.95	**104**	**135 B**
	Incentive, N.Sponsor (93-P)	N/A	**	**
	J.W. Collection (88)	36.95	**282**	**500 B**
	Regular Line(2sw/h) (79-P)	17.95		
18^L x 11^W x 4.5^H	Retired(1st/h) (80-93)	41.95	**77**	**120 B**
Gathering, Small	Easter (87)	28.95	**92**	**105 B**
	Employee Christmas(90)	N/A	**110**	**140 B**
	Incentive, N.Sponsor (93-P)	N/A	**	**
	Shades of Autumn(91)	48.95	**146**	**245 C**
	Regular Line(2sw/h) (79-P)	15.95		
14^L x 9^W x 4.5^H	Retired(1st/h) (86-93)	22.95	**74**	**80 B**
Getaway	Feature, Heartland (90)	65.95	**140**	**160 B**
	Sweetheart (90)	79.95	**144**	**180 B**
17^L x 14^W x 11^H	Sweetheart (93)	139.95	**155**	**190 B**
Gift Giving 20.5^L x 15^W x 10.5^H	Holiday Hostess (92)	169.85	**165**	**250 C**
Gingerbread 10^L x 6^W x 4^H	Christmas (90)	50.85	**110**	**135 C**
Gold Nugget 4.5^{RD} x 3^H	Incentive (94)	N/A	**178**	**235 B**
Gold Rush 6.5^{RD} x 4.75^H	Incentive (94)	N/A	**165**	**270 B**
Grandad Sleigh 9.25^L x 5.5^W x 2^{FH} x 5.5^{BH}	Christmas (82)	19.95	**720**	**850 B**
Hamper, Large	Feature (86)	79.95	**208**	**280 B**
	Feature (93-94)	185.95	**243**	**280 C**
	Hostess (86-90)	109.95	**220**	**275 B**
	Feature, SOA (91)	149.95	**220**	**250 B**
	Retired (79-86)	59.95	**211**	**290 B**
16.5^L x 16.5^W x 21.5^H				
Hamper, Large (1995 – P) 17^L x 17^W x 22^H	Regular Line, Hostess (95-P)	219.95		

KEY: * Market Values listed are the AVG and the HIGH Market Values.
C = Combo, **P** = with Protector, **L** = with Liner, **(-P)** = to present

Page in Guide	Form No.	Other Baskets Using Same Form
page 62	2400-C	None
page 68	2400-AGRS	
page 78	2400-	
page 92	2400-ABT	
checklist	12416/2400-CO	
page 110	12408/2400-AO	
page 42	2300-AX	Advisor Recognition, 92 Bee, Tray, Pantry, 90 Employee Christmas
page 50	2300-	
page 78	2300-	
page 116	2300-CGUBS	
checklist	12319/2300-CO	
page 110	12301/2300-AO	
page 58	300-CCS	Large Picnic
page 124	300-CRS	
page 124	10359	
page 68	12700 /12718	Forever Yours
page 28	3400-ARST/AGST	88 Small Easter, 93 Large Easter, Small Chore, 91 Regional Sponsored Award, 95 Bee, $500 Million
page 88	unknown	Thyme
page 88	unknown	None
page 28	4900-Z	None
page 62	1600-OO	90-91 Sponsor
page 64	11622	
page 72	1600-DO	
page 64	1600-DS	
page 110	1600-DO	
checklist	11631	None

KEY: In green = Not pictured in the Guide.
HL = Heartland® Collection, **WT** = Woven Traditions®, **R** = Red, **G** = Green

Basket	Collection(Year)	Original Price	Market Values*	
Hamper, Medium	Hostess (86-90)	69.95	**135**	**165 B**
	Retired (79-86)	31.95	**140**	**175 B**
12^L x 12.25^W x 16.25^H				
Hamper, Small	Feature, SOA (91)	99.95	**153**	**160 B**
12^L x 12.25^W x 16.25^H				
Hanging, 13" Sq. Bottom	Retired (80-86)	35.95	**40**	**40 B**
13RD x 12.5^H				
Hanging, 11" Sq. Bottom	Retired (80-86)	29.95	**40**	**40 B**
11RD x 10.5^H				
Hanging, 9" Sq. Bottom	Retired (80-86)	22.95	**40**	**40 B**
9RD x 8.5^H				
Hanging, 7" Sq. Bottom	Retired (80-86)	15.95	**70**	**85 B**
7RD x 6.5^H				
Hanging, 5" Sq. Bottom	Retired (80-86)	14.95	**79**	**95 B**
5RD x 4.5^H				
Hanging, Woven Bottom	Retired (79-86)	14.95	**85**	**100 B**
8.25^{RD} x 7.75^H				
Hartville Basket see **Tour**			**	
8.75^L x 4.75^W x 6.5^H				
Hartville II Basket see **Tour II**			**	
7^L x 3.5^W x 4.75^H				
Harvest	Hostess (90-92)	66.90	**90**	**105 P**
16^L x 9^W x 6^H				
Harvest (1993)	Shades of Autumn (93)	49.95	**105**	**145 C**
7^L x 4.75^W x 7.75^H				

KEY: * Market Values listed are the AVG and the HIGH Market Values.
C = Combo, **P** = with Protector, **L** = with Liner, **(-P)** = to present

Page in Guide	Form No.	Other Baskets Using Same Form
page 72 page 110	1700-DO 1700-DO	Small Hamper, 90-91 Recruit, 90-91 Sponsor (Superstar), Medium Waste
page 64	1700-DS	Medium Hamper, 90-91 Recruit, 90-91 Sponsor (Superstar), Medium Waste
page 110	4200-PO	13" Measuring
page 110	4100-PO	11" Measuring
page 110	4000-PO	9" Measuring, 9" Canister
page 110	3900-PO	90 Bee, Poinsettia, 7" Measuring, 92 Sponsor (Large), Maple Leaf, 7" Canister
page 110	3800-PO	88 Employee Birthday, Resolution 92 Employee Christmas, Forget-Me-Not, 5" Hanging, 5" Measuring, 92 Recruit, 92 Sponsor (Small), 5"Canister
page 110	3700-PO	None
page 92	15661	Tour, 89 Bee, 92 Employee Birthday Junior & Sophomore Recognition, Flag, Dresden Basket, Memory
page 92	15814	Tour II
page 72	3700-AOS	Original Easter, Senior Employee, 90 Bee Speaker
page 116	14303	None

KEY: In green = Not pictured in the Guide.
HL = Heartland® Collection, **WT** = Woven Traditions®, **R** = Red, **G** = Green

Basket	Collection (Year)	Original Price	Market Values*	
Hearthside 11.75^{RD} x 6.5^{H}	Hostess (90-92)	68.90	**105**	**140 P**
Heirloom 15^{L} x 10^{W} x 7.5^{H}	Hostess (90-92)	87.95	**133**	**180 B**
Herb 11.5^{L} x 5^{W} x 3^{H}	Feature (86)	32.90set	**72**	**95 B**
	Incentive (87-88)	N/A	**80**	**80 B**
High Achiever 12RD x 5.75^{H}	Incentive (95-96)	N/A	**	**
Holiday Cheer 12^{L} x 8^{W} x 4.25^{H}	Christmas (96)	59.95	**70**	**88 C**
Holly 15^{L} x 8^{W} x 2.25^{H}	Christmas (84)	24.95	**320**	**390 B**
Homecoming 15^{L} x 15^{W} x 7.5^{H}	Holiday Hostess (93)	149.95	**172**	**265 C**
Horizon of Hope (1995) 5.75^{L} x 3.75^{W} x 3^{H}	Feature (95)	41.85	**65**	**90 C**
Horizon of Hope (1996) 6.75^{L} x 4.75^{W} x 2.25^{H}	Feature (96)	41.85	**57**	**65 C**
Hostess Appreciation 8^{L} x 4^{W} x 2^{H}	Feature (94)	N/A	**74**	**120 B**
Hostess Appreciation 5.5^{L} x 5.5^{W} x 2.5^{H}	Feature (96)	N/A	**72**	**85 B**
Inaugural, (1989) 5RD x 4.5^{H}	Special Event (89)	19.89	**176**	**300 B**

KEY: * Market Values listed are the AVG and the HIGH Market Values.
C = Combo, **P** = with Protector, **L** = with Liner, **(-P)** = to present

Page in Guide	Form No.	Other Baskets Using Same Form
page 72	42000-AOS	None
page 72	500-HOS	88 Bee Speaker, 87 Employee Christmas, Medium Market, (77-87) Tenth Anniversary
page 62 page 82	4500-AO 4500-	Liberty, Bed, Cracker, Muffin 96 Employee Christmas
page 88	unknown	Basket of Plenty, Quilting
page 30	18520 / 18511	None
page 28	4600-AZ	Bread (old), Garden
page 70	12084 / 12092	Medium Picnic
page 64	17124	All-Star Trio, Keepsake, Paint the Town, 90 Recruit, Shining Star, Rosemary, Sugar and Spice, Treasure Chest, 90 Sweetheart, 95 Horizon of Hope
page 64	15911	None
page 64	unknown	93 Recruit, 93 Sponsor (Small), Lavender, Rose Bud
page 64	unknown	Ivy, 91 Employee Birthday, Friendship
page 120	3800-ABRST	88 Emp.Birthday, 92 Sponsor (Small) 92 Emp.Christmas, Forget-Me-Not, 5" Hanging, 5" Measuring, 92 Recruit, Resolution, 5" Canister

KEY: In green = Not pictured in the Guide.
HL = Heartland® Collection, **WT** = Woven Traditions®, **R** = Red, **G** = Green

Basket	Collection(Year)	Original Price	Market Values*	
Inaugural, (1993) $5^L \times 5^W \times 4.5^H$	Special Event (93)	34.95	**86**	**135 B**
Inaugural, (1997) $5.5^{RD} \times 3.25^H$	Special Event (97)	42.95	**53**	**60 C**
Ivy	Booking (90-92)	N/A	**52**	**67 L**
$5.5^L \times 5.5^W \times 2.5^H$	Employee (91)	N/A	**90**	**130 B**
Jingle Bell $8^{RD} \times 6^H$	Christmas (94)	59.95	**90**	**125 C**
Junior Recognition $8.75^L \times 4.75^W \times 6.5^H$	Employee	N/A	**79**	**85 B**
Keepsake $5.75^L \times 3.75^W \times 3^H$	Booking (88-90)	16.95	**50**	**75 B**
Key, Medium	Feature (94)	29.95	**43**	**50 B**
	Heartland(88-P)	26.95		
$9^L \times 5^W \times 5^H$	Regular Line (79-P)	9.95		
Key, Small	Feature (94)	27.95	**37**	**50 B**
	Heartland(94-P)	21.95		
$7^L \times 5^W \times 3.5^H$	Regular Line (79-P)	7.95		
Key, Tall	Employee Christmas(91)	N/A	**108**	**120 B**
	Feature (94)	40.95	**48**	**60 B**
	Heartland (88-P)	34.95		
	Holiday Hostess (88)	30.95	**92**	**125 B**
	Regular Line (79-P)	11.95		
$9.5^L \times 5^W \times 9.5^H$	Retired(Natrl) (94)	31.95	**42**	**50 B**

KEY: * Market Values listed are the AVG and the HIGH Market Values.
C = Combo, **P** = with Protector, **L** = with Liner, **(-P)** = to present

Page in Guide	Form No.	Other Baskets Using Same Form
page 120	11461	Candy Cane, Violet, Small Peg 96 Recruit, Tea Spoon
page 120	65323	None
page 24 page 48	13100-JOS 13100-	91 Employee Birthday, Friendship, 96 Hostess Appreciation
page 30	17906/17914	None
page 48	unknown	89 Bee, Dresden Basket, Tour, Flag, 92 Employee Birthday, Memory, Sophomore and Senior Recognition, Hartville Basket
page 24	45000-IO	All-Star Trio, 89 Employee Birthday Paint the Town, 90 Recruiting, Shining Star, Rosemary, Sugar and Spice, 90 Sweetheart, Treasure Chest, 95 Horizon of Hope
page 58 checklist checklist	15172/99/81 11118/1100-ICS 11100/1100-IO	Candle, 97 Renewal, 90 Sponsor 89 Employee Christmas, 96 Perfect Attendance
page 58 checklist, HL checklist	17078/51/60 10782/700-ICS 10723/700-IO	Acorn, Basket of Thanks, Tea, Mini Berry, Mini Chore, Mistletoe, Mini Cradle, Baby Easter, 91 Hostess Easter, 93 Small Easter, 94 Employee Christmas, Kiddie Purse, Star Team, Patriot
page 50 page 58 checklist, HL page 68 checklist page 110	1000- 14672/99/81 11061/1000-ICS 1000-IRGS 11053/1000-IO 14630	MBA, Tall Purse, Two-quart, Collectors Club Membership, 91 Employee Christmas

KEY: In green = Not pictured in the Guide.
HL = Heartland® Collection, **WT** = Woven Traditions®, **R** = Red, **G** = Green

Basket	Collection(Year)	Original Price	Market Values*	
Laundry, Large 30L x 20W x 10.5H	Hostess (86-90)	96.95	**183**	**275 B**
	Retired (79-86)	34.95	**182**	**250 B**
Laundry, Medium 28.5L x 17.75W x 9.75H	Retired (79-83)	31.95	—	—
Laundry, Small 24L x 17W x 10H	Holiday Hostess (88)	67.95	**270**	**350 B**
	Regular Line (79-P)	29.95		
Laurel 5.5RD x 3.75H	Booking (90-92)	N/A	**48**	**70 P**
Lavender 8L x 4W x 2H	Regular Line (92-P)	22.95		
Liberty 11.5L x 5W x 3H	All-American (93)	36.95	**70**	**95 C**
Lilac 6.5RD x 6.5H	May (94)	42.95	**88**	**130 C**
Lily of the Valley 5.5RD x 3.75H	May (93)	39.95	**80**	**135 C**
Magazine 16L x 8W x 11H	Holiday Hostess (89)	53.95	**117**	**160 B**
	Regular Line(2sw/h) (79-P)	21.95		
	Regular Line(1sw/h, legs) (79-P)	25.95		
	Retired(1sw/h, legs, no lid) (79-95)	21.95	**83**	**100 B**
Mail 12L x 8W x 11.5H	Hostess (92-96)	106.95	**126**	**160 C**
Maple Leaf 7RD x 6.5H	Shades of Autumn (96)	54.95	**71**	**90 C**
Market, Large 16L x 11W x 9H	Feature (96)	92.43 C	—	—
	Holiday Hostess (88)	49.95	**114**	**140 C**
	Regular Line(2sw/h) (83-P)	29.95		
	Retired(1st/h) (79-93)	19.95	**76**	**105 B**

KEY: * Market Values listed are the AVG and the HIGH Market Values.
C = Combo, **P** = with Protector, **L** = with Liner, **(-P)** = to present

Page in Guide	Form No.	Other Baskets Using Same Form
page 72 page 110	2800-O 2800-OO	Large Cradle
page 110	2700-O	Medium Cradle
page 68 checklist	2600-ORGS 12602 /2600-OO	Family Picnic, Small Cradle
page 24	17000-JOS	Basket 'O Luck, Pot of Gold, Lily of Valley
checklist, Booking	10138	94 Hostess Appreciation, 93 Recruit 93 Sponsor (Small), Rose Bud
page 16	14541	Bed, Cracker, Herb, Muffin 96 Employee Christmas
page 97	16209	Bouquet
page 97	15717	Basket of Luck, Laurel, Pot of Gold
page 68 checklist checklist page 112	2100-CGRS 12106/2100-CO 12114 12122/2100-U	Bread & Milk
page 72	10600	None
page 116	13935	7″ Measuring, 90 Bee, Poinsettia, 92 Sponsor (Large), 7″ Hanging, 7″ Canister
page 60 page 68 checklist page 112	16641/24/32 600-ARGS 10634/600-CO 10626/600-AO	Rectangular Sewing

KEY: In green = Not pictured in the Guide.
HL = Heartland® Collection, **WT** = Woven Traditions®, **R** = Red, **G** = Green

Basket	Collection (Year)	Original Price	Market Values*	
Market, Medium	Employee Christmas (87)	N/A	**235**	**310 B**
	Feature (Natrl) (87)	41.95	—	—
	Heartland (89-P)	43.95		
	J.W. Collection (83)	32.95	**1211**	**1550 B**
	Regular Line(1st/h) (79-P)	16.95		
$15^{L} \times 10^{W} \times 7.5^{H}$	Regular Line (2sw/h) (83-P)	24.95		
Market, Miniature $5.75^{L} \times 4^{W} \times 3^{H}$	Collectors Club (96)	141.90	**232**	**310 C**
Market, Small	All-American (92)	54.95	**122**	**175 C**
	Regular Line(2sw/h) (93-P)	45.95		
$15^{L} \times 9.5^{W} \times 5.5^{H}$	Retired(1st/h) (79-93)	14.95	**67**	**125 B**
Master Employee $12.5^{RD} \times 13.5^{H}$	Employee	N/A	**232**	**275 B**
MBA Basket $9.5^{L} \times 5^{W} \times 9.5^{H}$	Incentive (88-P)	N/A	**198**	**220 B**
Meadow Blossoms Pottery	Incentive (85)	N/A	**	**
Measuring, 13"	Holiday Hostess (90)	69.95	**123**	**155 B**
$13^{RD} \times 12.5^{H}$	Regular Line (79-P)	20.95		
Measuring, 11"	Incentive, N.Sales (94-P)	N/A	**	**
$11^{RD} \times 10.5^{H}$	Regular Line (79-P)	17.95		
Measuring, 9"	Incentive, N.Sales (94-P)	N/A	**	**
$9^{RD} \times 8.5^{H}$	Regular Line (79-P)	13.95		
Measuring, 7"	Incentive, N.Sales (94-P)	N/A	**	**
$7^{RD} \times 6.5^{H}$	Regular Line (79-P)	33.95		
Measuring, 5"	Booking (xx-84)	N/A	—	—
	Employee Birthday (88)	N/A	**77**	**105 B**
	Employee Christmas(92)	N/A	**94**	**120 B**
	Incentive, N.Sales (94-P)	N/A	**	**
$5^{RD} \times 4.5^{H}$	Regular Line (79-P)	7.95		

KEY: * Market Values listed are the AVG and the HIGH Market Values.
C = Combo, **P** = with Protector, **L** = with Liner, **(-P)** = to present

Page in Guide	Form No.	Other Baskets Using Same Form
page 50	500-A	88 Bee Speaker, Heirloom,
page 62	500-	77-87 Tenth Anniversary, 87
checklist	10545/500-ACS	Employee Christmas
page 92	500-AT	
checklist	10529/500-AO	
checklist	10537	
page 32	15024/150240	None
page 14	10707	None
checklist	10430/400-CO	
page 112	10421/400-AO	
page 48	1900-	Banker's Waste, Waste (Inverted, Small Round) , Tree-Trimming
page 84	1000-FO	91 Employee Christmas, Tall Key, Tall Purse, Two-Quart, Collectors Club Membership
	unknown	None
page 68	4200-CGRS	13" Hanging
checklist	14206/4200-PO	
page 80	unknown	11" Hanging
checklist	14109/4100-BO	
page 80	unknown	9" Hanging, 9" Canister
checklist	14001/4000-BO	
page 80	unknown	90 Bee, Maple Leaf, Poinsettia,
checklist	13901/3900-BO	92 Sponsor (Large), 7" Hanging
page 24	3800-BO	89 Inaugural, Forget-Me-Not
page 48	3800-	5" Hanging, 92 Recruit, Resolution,
page 50	3800-	92 Sponsor (Small), 5" Canister,
page 80	unknown	92 Employee Christmas, 88
checklist	13803/3800-BO	Employee Birthday

Basket	Collection (Year)	Original Price	Market Values*	
Memory	Christmas (89)	34.95	**86**	**135 B**
	Feature (88-89)	39.95	**162**	**180 B**
8.75^{L} x 4.75^{W} x 6.5^{H}				
Mistletoe	Christmas (87)	19.95	**115**	**180 B**
7^{L} x 5^{W} x 3.5^{H}				
Mother's Day (1992)	Mother's Day (92)	49.95	**94**	**140 C**
10.5^{L} x 10.5^{W} x 4.5^{H}				
Mother's Day (1993)	Mother's Day (93)	57.95	**115**	**130 C**
8.5^{L} x 8^{W} x 6^{H}				
Mother's Day (1994)	Mother's Day (94)	49.95	**75**	**115 C**
6.75^{L} x 9.25^{W} x 3.75^{H}				
Mother's Day (1995)	Mother's Day (95)	49.95	**70**	**100 C**
8.5^{RD} x 4^{H}				
Mother's Day (1996)	Mother's Day (96)	59.95	**79**	**110 C**
13.5^{L} x 7.5^{W} x 4.5^{FH} x 6.5^{BH}				
Muffin	Heartland (90-P)	25.95		
11.5^{L} x 5^{W} x 3^{H}				
Odds & Ends	Regular Line (95-P)	149.95		
18.75^{L} x 9^{W} x 12.75^{FH} x 5.25^{BH}				
Original Easter	J.W. Collection (93)	82.95	**165**	**220 C**
16^{L} x 9^{W} x 6^{H}				
Over the Rainbow (small) see **Gold Nugget**				
Over the Rainbow (medium) see **Pot of Gold**				

KEY: * Market Values listed are the AVG and the HIGH Market Values.
C = Combo, **P** = with Protector, **L** = with Liner, **(-P)** = to present

Page in Guide	Form No.	Other Baskets Using Same Form
page 28 page 58	5600-BRST/BGST 5600-BBS	89 Bee, Dresden Basket, Hartville Basket, Tour, 92 Employee Birthday, Junior and Sophomore Recognition, Flag
page 28	700-ART/AGT	Acorn, Basket of Thanks, Tea, Mini Berry, Mini Chore, Patriot, Mini Cradle, Baby Easter, 91 Hostess Easter, Small Key, 93 Small Easter, 94 Employee Christmas, Kiddie Purse, Star Team
page 100	110-CPS	None
page 100	12904	None
page 100	16004	None
page 100	18805	Best Supporting Role
page 100	14753	None
checklist, HL	14516/4500-JCS	Liberty, Bed, Cracker, Herb 96 Employee Christmas
checklist, Hostess	18902	None
page 92	13722	Harvest, Senior Employee, 90 Bee Speaker
page 88	unknown	None
page 88	unknown	Lily of the Valley, Basket O'Luck, Laurel

KEY: In green = Not pictured in the Guide.
HL = Heartland® Collection, **WT** = Woven Traditions®, **R** = Red, **G** = Green

Basket	Collection(Year)	Original Price	Market Values*	
Over the Rainbow (large) see **Gold Rush**				
Paint the Town	Incentive (93)	N/A	**119**	**185 B**
$5.75^L \times 3.75^W \times 3^H$				
Pansy	May (92)	39.95	**116**	**185 C**
$7^{RD} \times 4.5^H$				
Pantry	Feature (85)	21.95	**55**	**70 B**
	Feature (96)	55.93	—	—
$14^L \times 9^W \times 4.5^H$	Regular Line (86-P)	21.95		
Paper	Father's Day (92)	33.95	**115**	**150 C**
	Incentive (92-P)	N/A	**65**	**75 B**
$7.5^L \times 5.5^W \times 2^{FH} \times 3.5^{BH}$				
Patriot	All-American (97)	44.95	—	—
$7^L \times 5^W \times 3.5^H$				
Peg, Large	Bee (88)	N/A	—	—
	Heartland (89-P)	28.95		
	Mother's Day (87)	26.95	**119**	**160 C**
	Regular Line (85-P)	19.95		
$6.5^L \times 6.5^W \times 8^H$	Woven Traditions (95-P)	39.95		
Peg, Medium	Bee (88)	N/A	—	—
	Feature (shaker) (84)	14.95	**45**	**60 B**
$5.5^L \times 5.5^W \times 6^H$	Regular Line (85-P)	17.95		
Peg, Small	Bee (88)	N/A	—	—
	Regular Line (85-P)	15.95		
$5^L \times 5^W \times 4.5^H$				
Pencil	Father's Day (92)	29.95	**127**	**175 C**
	Incentive (92-P)	N/A	**70**	**75 B**
$4^{RD} \times 4.25^H$				

KEY: * Market Values listed are the AVG and the HIGH Market Values.
C = Combo, **P** = with Protector, **L** = with Liner, **(-P)** = to present

Page in Guide	Form No.	Other Baskets Using Same Form
page 88	unknown	None
page 86	45000-	All-Star Trio, 89 Employee Birthday, Keepsake, 90 Recruit, Shining Star, Rosemary, Sugar and Spice, 90 Sweetheart, Treasure Chest, 95 Horizon of Hope
page 97	10006	Perfect Attendance (95)
page 60 page 60 checklist	2300-JO 16446/20/38 12327/ 2300-JO	Advisor Recognition, 92 Bee, 90 Employee Christmas,Tray, Small Gathering
page 54 page 82	16000 16000	None
page 16	10651	Acorn, Basket of Thanks, Mini Berry, Mini Chore, Mistletoe, Mini Cradle, Baby Easter, 91 Hostess Easter, 93 Small Easter, Star Team, 94 Employee Christmas, Kiddie Purse, Small Key, Tea
page 20 checklist page 100 checklist checklist	11000-AO 11177/11000-ACS 11000-BPS 11151 /11000-AO 11142	Medium Spoon, 94 Bee
page 20 page 60 checklist	10000-AO 10000-AO 11070 /10000-AO	Bittersweet, Carry-Along, Small Spoon, 96 Sponsor, Shaker Peg
page 20 checklist	14000-AO 11452 /14000-ART	93 Inaugural, Candy Cane, Violet, 96 Recruit, Tea Spoon
page 54 page 82	15000 15000-	None

KEY: In green = Not pictured in the Guide.
HL = Heartland® Collection, **WT** = Woven Traditions®, **R** = Red, **G** = Green

Basket	Collection(Year)	Original Price	Market Values*	
Perfect Attendance (1994) 6.5RD x 5H	Employee (94)	N/A	**420**	**425 B**
Perfect Attendance (1995) 7RD x 4.5H	Employee (95)	N/A	**400**	**450 B**
Perfect Attendance (1996) 9L x 5W x 5H	Employee (96)	N/A	--	—
Personal Organizer 14L x 6W x 3H	Father's Day (97)	54.95 C	—	—
Petunia 9.5RD x 5H	May (97)	59.95	—	—
Picnic, Family 24L x 17W x 10H	Retired (83-86)	135.90	**331**	**390 L**
Picnic, Gourmet 13.25L x 11.25W x 9H	Hostess (92-95)	132.85	**140**	**175 C**
Picnic, Large	All-American (87)	64.95	**273**	**365 B**
17L x 14W x 11H	Regular Line (79-P)	29.95		
Picnic, Medium 15L x 15W x 7.5H	Retired (79-84)	26.95	**190**	**200 B**
Picnic, Oak Lid 12L x 12W x 6H	Feature (82)	N/A	**467**	**600 B**
Picnic, Small	All-American (88)	65.95	**178**	**225 B**
12L x 12W x 6H	Regular Line (79-P)	21.95		
Pie	Easter (87)	28.95	**97**	**115 B**
	Regular Line (86-P)	22.95		
	Shades of Autumn (90)	31.95	**118**	**150 B**
	Feature, W.Tradition (94)	79.95	**80**	**95 C**
12L x 12W x 4H	Feature (85)	19.95		
Pie, Crisco 12L x 12W x 6H	Crisco® (91)	89.90	**368**	**510 P**

KEY: * Market Values listed are the AVG and the HIGH Market Values.
C = Combo, **P** = with Protector, **L** = with Liner, **(-P)** = to present

Page in Guide	Form No.	Other Baskets Using Same Form
page 48	unknown	Small Fruit
page 48	unknown	Pansy
page 48	unknown	Candle, 90 Sponsor, Medium Key, 97 Renewal, 89 Employee Christmas
page 54	63134	Flower Pot (Small)
page 97	12947	90 Large Easter
page 112	2600-HO	Small Laundry, Small Cradle
page 72	10413	Precious Treasures
page 14 checklist	300-HBRS 10324 /300-HO	Getaway
page 112	200-H	Homecoming
page 60	unknown	Cake, Crisco Pie, 88 Employee Christmas, Small Picnic
page 14 checklist	100-HBRS 10324 /300-HO	Cake, Crisco Pie, 88 Employee Christmas, Oak Lid Picnic
page 42 checklist page 116 page 58 page 60	2200-AX 12203 /2200-AO 2200-AGUBS 12211 2200-AO	None
page 40	100-DBRS	Cake, 88 Employee Christmas, Small Picnic, Oak Lid Picnic

KEY: In green = Not pictured in the Guide.
HL = Heartland® Collection, **WT** = Woven Traditions®, **R** = Red, **G** = Green

Basket	Collection(Year)	Original Price	Market Values*	
Planter, Large Fern	Feature(feet) (88)	42.95	**140**	**140 B**
	Retired(feet) (82-86)	27.95	**120**	**180 B**
	Retired(13") (79-86)	23.95	**121**	**200 B**
13RD x 8.5H	Retired(20") (79-86)	26.95	—	**130 B**
Planter, Small Fern	Feature(feet) (88)	35.95	**125**	**140 B**
	Retired(feet) (82-86)	21.95	**97**	**175 B**
	Retired(13") (79-86)	21.95	**115**	**130 B**
8.5RD x 7.5H	Retired(20") (79-86)	24.95	**138**	**150 B**
Planter, Patio 10RD x 5.5H	Feature (84)	21.95	**88**	**105 B**
Planter, Sleeve 31.5RD x 18H	Incentive (91)	N/A	**445**	**500 B**
Precious Treasures 13.25L x 11.25W x 9H	Sweetheart (95)	99.95	**170**	**200 C**
Poinsettia 7RD x 6.5H	Christmas (88)	26.95	**102**	**155 B**
Pot of Gold 5.5RD x 3.75H	Incentive (94)	N/A		
Potpourri	Booking (85-90)	3.00	**55**	**80 B**
	Employee Birthday(90)	N/A	**75**	**100 B**
5L x 5W x 2.5H	Mother's Day (91)	30.90	**80**	**125 C**
Pumpkin 9.25RD x 7.25H	Feature (95)	59.95	**95**	**125 C**
Pumpkin, Small 7.25RD x 5.25H	Feature (96)	52.95	**73**	**90 C**
Purse, Kiddie	Regular Line (79-P)	12.95		
7L x 5W x 3.5H	Retired(Natrl) (94)	28.95	**41**	**50 B**
Purse, Medium	Regular Line(1sw/h) (79-P)	16.95		
11L x 8W x 5.5H	Retired(split lid) (82-86)	24.95	**123**	**255 B**

KEY: * Market Values listed are the AVG and the HIGH Market Values.
C = Combo, **P** = with Protector, **L** = with Liner, **(-P)** = to present

Page in Guide	Form No.	Other Baskets Using Same Form
page 64 page 112 page 112 page 112	3200-RO 3200-RO 3200-SO 3200-TO	Large Fruit, Sewing (Round) Apple
page 64 page 112 page 112 page 112	2900-RO 2900-RO 2900-SO 2900-TO	None
page 60	6000-R	None
page 82	unknown	None
page 124	10456	Gourmet Picnic
page 28	3900-BRST/BGST	90 Bee, 7" Hanging, 7" Measuring, 92 Sponsor (Large), Maple Leaf
page 88	unknown	Basket O' Luck, Laurel, Lily of Valley
page 24 page 48 page 100	13000-AO 13000- 13000-APS	88-89 Recruit, 90 Employee Birthday 93 Regional Sponsored Award, Sweet Basil, 93 Sweetheart, Shamrock
page 58	19402	None
page 58	16012	None
checklist page 112	10731 / 700-EO 17019	Acorn, Basket of Thanks, Tea, Mini Berry, Mini Chore, Mistletoe, Mini Cradle, Baby Easter, Patriot, 91 Hostess Easter, 93 Small Easter, Small Key, 94 Employee Christmas, Star Team
checklist page 112	10901 900-QO	91-P Bee Speaker, Bob and Dolores Hope, Boo Basket, 91 Customer Easter, Red Pottery Thank You, Spring, Statehouse

KEY: In green = Not pictured in the Guide.
HL = Heartland® Collection, **WT** = Woven Traditions®, **R** = Red, **G** = Green

Basket	Collection(Year)	Original Price	Market Values*	
Purse, Shoulder $9.5^L \times 6^W \times 7^H$	Regular Line (96-P)	84.95		
Purse, Small	Heartland (88-P)	36.95		
	Mother's Day (91)	54.85	**120**	**150 B**
$9.5^L \times 6^W \times 6^H$	Regular Line (79-P)	14.95		
Purse, Tall $9.5^L \times 5^W \times 9.5^H$	Retired (79-89)	27.95	**117**	**160 B**
Quilting $12^{RD} \times 5.75^H$	All-American (89)	46.95	**165**	**210 B**
Reach for the Stars(Small) see **Star Bound** $4.75^L \times 3.75^W \times 2.25^H$				
Reach for the Stars(Medium) see **Shining Star** $5.75^L \times 3.75^W \times 3^H$				
Reach for the Stars(Large) see **Star Team** $7^L \times 5^W \times 3.5^H$				
Recipe	Regular Line (96-P)	29.95		
	Shades of Autumn (94)	44.95	**135**	**145 C**
$8^L \times 5.5^W \times 4.5^{FH} \times 6^{BH}$				
Recruit **"Share the Tradition"** $5^L \times 5^W \times 2.5^H$	Incentive (88-89)	N/A	**170**	**220 B**
Recruit **"Together–We're Growing"** $5.75^L \times 3.75^W \times 3^H$	Incentive (90)	N/A	**169**	**180 B**

KEY: * Market Values listed are the AVG and the HIGH Market Values.
C = Combo, **P** = with Protector, **L** = with Liner, **(-P)** = to present

Page in Guide	Form No.	Other Baskets Using Same Form
checklist	18210	None
checklist page 100 checklist	10839/800-ECS 800-EPS 10821/800-EO	Season's Greetings, 94 Regional Sponsored
page 112	1000-EO	91 Employee Christmas, MBA, Tall Key, Two-Quart, Collectors Club Membership
page 14	54000-ABRS	Basket of Plenty, High Achiever
page 88	unknown	Business Card
page 88	unknown	All-Star Trio, 89 Employee Birthday, Keepsake, Paint the Town, 90 Recruit, Rosemary, Sugar and Spice, 90 Sweetheart, Treasure Chest, 95 Horizon of Hope
page 88	unknown	Acorn, Basket of Thanks, Tea, Mini Berry, Mini Chore, Mistletoe, Mini Cradle, Baby Easter, Patriot, 91 Hostess Easter, 93 Small Easter, 94 Employee Christmas, Kiddie Purse, Small Key
checklist, Hostess page 116	17418 17400	None
page 76	13000-BBRS	90 Employee Birthday, 93 Regional Sponsored Award, 93 Sweetheart, Potpourri, Shamrock, Sweet Basil
page 76	45000-ABRST	All-Star Trio, 89 Employee Birthday, Keepsake, Paint the Town, Shining Star, Rosemary, Sugar and Spice, 90 Sweetheart, Treasure Chest, 95 Horizon of Hope

KEY: In green = Not pictured in the Guide.
HL = Heartland® Collection, **WT** = Woven Traditions®, **R** = Red, **G** = Green

Basket	Collection (Year)	Original Price	Market Values*	
Recruit **"Rising Star"** 12^{L} x 12.25^{W} x 16.25^{H}	Incentive (90-91)	N/A	**175**	**175 B**
Recruit **"Flying High with Longaberger"** 5RD x 4.5^{H}	Incentive (92)	N/A	**119**	**125 B**
Recruit **"All-Star"** 8^{L} x 4^{W} x 2^{H}	Incentive (93)	N/A	**135**	**200 B**
Recruit **"Pegged for Success"** 5^{L} x 5^{W} x 4.5^{H}	Incentive (96)	N/A	—	—
Red Pottery **Thank You** 11^{L} x 8^{W} x 5.5^{H}	Feature (93)	N/A	**126**	**150 B**
Regional Basket 15.75^{L} x 6.5^{W} x 11^{H}	Incentive (88-P)	N/A	**250**	**250 B**
Regional **Sponsored (1991)** 10^{L} x 6^{W} x 4^{H}	Incentive (91)	N/A	**175**	**200 B**
Regional **Sponsored (1992)** 8.5^{L} x 5^{W} x 3.5^{H}	Incentive (92)	N/A	**195**	**275 B**
Regional **Sponsored (1993)** 5^{L} x 5^{W} x 2.5^{H}	Incentive (93)	N/A	**187**	**275 B**
Regional **Sponsored (1994)** 9.5^{L} x 6^{W} x 6^{H}	Incentive (94)	N/A	**226**	**250 B**
Regional **Sponsored (1995)** 7.5^{L} x 7.5^{W} x 3.5^{H}	Incentive (95)	N/A	**234**	**250 B**

KEY: * Market Values listed are the AVG and the HIGH Market Values.
C = Combo, **P** = with Protector, **L** = with Liner, **(-P)** = to present

Page in Guide	Form No.	Other Baskets Using Same Form
page 76	1700-DST	Medium Hamper, Small Hamper, 90-91 Sponsor (Superstar), Medium Waste
page 76	10154	88 Emp.Birthday, 89 Inaugural, 5" Measuring, Forget-Me-Not, 92 Emp. Christmas, 5" Hanging, Resolution, 92 Sponsor (Small)
page 76	16101	94 Hostess Appreciation, Rose Bud, 93 Sponsor (Small), Lavender
page 76	unknown	93 Inaugural, Candy Cane, Violet, Small Peg, Tea Spoon
page 58	190xx	91- P Bee Speaker, Bob & Dolores Hope, Boo Basket, 91 Customer Easter, Medium Purse, Spring, 96 Statehouse
page 84	unknown	Branch Basket, Director Basket
page 86	3400-	Small Chore, 93 Large Easter, 88 Small Easter, Gingerbread, 95 Bee, $500 Million
page 86	33000-	Be Mine, Small Oval, 93 Sponsor (Large), 97 Small Easter, Rose Petal
page 86	11321	Sweet Basil, 90 Employee Birthday, Shamrock, 93 Sweetheart, 88-89 Recruit, Potpourri
page 86	800-	Season's Greetings, Small Purse
page 86	1400-	Medium Berry

KEY: In green = Not pictured in the Guide.
HL = Heartland® Collection, **WT** = Woven Traditions®, **R** = Red, **G** = Green

Basket	Collection (Year)	Original Price	Market Values*	
Regional Sponsored (1996) 10RD x 4H	Incentive (96)	N/A	**234**	**250 B**
Remembrance 10.5L x 9W x 8H	Feature (96)	112.93 C	—	—
	Hostess (90-92)	88.90	169	240 P
Resolution 5RD x 4.5H	Feature (87)	16.95	**117**	**150 B**
Rose 14.5L x 7.5W x 3.75H	May (91)	39.95	**182**	**285 C**
Rose Bud 8L x 4W x 2H	Incentive (97)	N/A	—	—
Rose Garden 12L x 7W x 4.5H	Incentive (97)	N/A	—	—
Rose Petal 8.5L x 5W x 3.5H	Incentive (97)	N/A	—	—
Rosemary 5.75L x 3.75W x 3H	Booking (90-92)	N/A	**56**	**70 P**
Season's Greetings 9.5L x 6W x 6H	Christmas (92)	53.95	**92**	**130 C**
Senior Employee 16L x 9W x 6H	Employee	N/A	**92**	**125 B**
Senior Recognition 8.75L x 4.75W x 6.5H	Employee	N/A	**85**	**125 B**
Serving Tray 20L x 14W x 3.75H	Regular Line (92-P)	74.95		

KEY: * Market Values listed are the AVG and the HIGH Market Values.
C = Combo, **P** = with Protector, **L** = with Liner, **(-P)** = to present

Page in Guide	Form No.	Other Baskets Using Same Form
page 86	500-	Darning, Crisco Cookie, Daisy, 89 Easter
page 60 page 72	16648/21/30 200-YOS	Weekender, Top Performer
page 58	3800-ABS	88 Employee Birthday, 89 Inaugural, 92 Employee Christmas, Forget-Me-Not, 5" Hanging, 5" Measuring, 92 Recruit, 92 Sponsor (Small), 5″ Canister
page 97	4700-CSS	Bakery, Bread (new), Breakfast, Crisco Baking
page 88	unknown	Lavender, 94 Hostess Appreciation 93 Recruit, 93 Sponsor (Small)
page 86	unknown	97 Large Easter
page 88	unknown	Be Mine, 93 Sponsor (All-Star), 92 Regional Sponsored Award, 97 Small Easter, Small Oval
page 24	45000-JOS	All-Star Trio, 89 Employee Birthday, Keepsake, Paint the Town, 90 Recruit, Reach for the Stars (Med.), Sugar and Spice, 90 Sweetheart, Treasure Chest, 95 Horizon of Hope
page 28	10316 / 10219	Small Purse, 94 Regional Sponsored
page 48	unknown	Original Easter, Harvest, 90 Bee Speaker
page 48	unknown	89 Bee, 92 Emp.Birthday, Hartville, Junior & Sophomore Recognition, Memory, Flag, Tour, Dresden
checklist, Hostess	60011	None

KEY: In green = Not pictured in the Guide.
HL = Heartland® Collection, **WT** = Woven Traditions®, **R** = Red, **G** = Green

Basket	Collection(Year)	Original Price	Market Values*	
Serving Tray, Small 11.5^L x 15.5^W x 3.75^H	Collectors Club (96)	102.85	**175**	**200 C**
Sewing, Rectangular 16^L x 11^W x 9^H	Retired (78-83)	26.95	**381**	**400 B**
Sewing, Round 13RD x 8.5^H	Feature (no stand) (85, 87)	37.95	**160**	**190 B**
	Regular Line (95-P)	89.95		
	Retired (78-86)	29.95	**	**
Shamrock 5^L x 5^W x 2.5^H	Feature (90)	19.95	**118**	**150 B**
Shining Star 5.75^L x 3.75^W x 3^H	Incentive (95)	N/A	**185**	**300 B**
Show Star 7RD x 3^H	Incentive (96)	N/A	**118**	**160 B**
Sleigh Bell 16.5RD x 11.5^H	Holiday Hostess (94)	199.95	**182**	**250 C**
Small Oval 8.5^L x 5^W x 3.5^H	Mother's Day (90)	36.90	**100**	**110 C**
Sophomore Recognition 8.75^L x 4.75^W x 6.5^H	Employee (xx-P)	N/A	**67**	**75 B**
Spare Change 6.5^L x 6.5^W x 3^H	Father's Day (91)	32.95	**115**	**150 C**
Sponsor "Share the Tradition" 8.5^L x 8.5^W x 5^H	Incentive (88-89)	N/A	**193**	**325 B**
Sponsor "Together–We're Growing" 9^L x 5^W x 5^H	Incentive (90)	N/A	**175**	**200 B**

KEY: * Market Values listed are the AVG and the HIGH Market Values.
C = Combo, **P** = with Protector, **L** = with Liner, **(-P)** = to present

Page in Guide	Form No.	Other Baskets Using Same Form
page 32	12629	None
page 114	600-F	Large Market
page 60 checklist, Hostess page 112	3200-EO 13234 3200-NO	Large Fruit, Apple, Planter (Large Fern)
page 58	13000-HGS	90 Employee Birthday, Sweet Basil, 93 Sweetheart, Potpourri, 93 Regional Sponsored Award, 88-89 Recruit
page 88	unknown	All-Star Trio, 89 Employee Birthday, Keepsake, Paint the Town, 90 Recruit, Sugar and Spice, Treasure Chest, Rosemary, 90 Sweetheart, 95 Horizon of Hope
page 88	unknown	Button, Cookie, Stitching, 93 Employee Christmas
page 70	14427[R] / 14435[G]	None
page 100	33000-JPS	Be Mine, 93 Sponsor (All-Star), 92 Regional Sponsored Award, 97 Small Easter, Rose Petal
page 48	unknown	89 Bee, Dresden Basket, Tour, Flag, 92 Employee Birthday, Memory, Junior and Senior Recognition, Hartville Basket,
page 54	1300-JCWS	Small Berry
page 76	1500-BBRS	91 Bee, Large Berry, 96 Bee
page 76	1100-ABRST	89 Employee Christmas, Candle, Medium Key, 97 Renewal, 96 Perfect Attendance

KEY: In green = Not pictured in the Guide.
HL = Heartland® Collection, **WT** = Woven Traditions®, **R** = Red, **G** = Green

Basket	Collection (Year)	Original Price	Market Values*	
Sponsor **"Rising Star"** $16.5^L \times 16.5^W \times 21.5^H$	Incentive (90-91)	N/A	**185**	**230 B**
Sponsor, Superstar **"Rising Star"** $12^L \times 12.25^W \times 16.25^H$	Incentive (90-91)	N/A	**155**	**200 B**
Sponsor, Large **"Flying High with Longaberger"** $7^{RD} \times 6.5^H$	Incentive (92)	N/A	**125**	**175 B**
Sponsor, Small **"Flying High with Longaberger"** $5^{RD} \times 4.5^H$	Incentive (92)	N/A	**118**	**175 B**
Sponsor, Large **"All-Star"** $8.5^L \times 5^W \times 3.5^H$	Incentive (93)	N/A	**130**	**165 B**
Sponsor, Small **"All-Star"** $8^L \times 4^W \times 2^H$	Incentive (93)	N/A	**113**	**160 B**
Sponsor **"Pegged for Success"** $5.5^L \times 5.5^W \times 6^H$	Incentive (96)	N/A	—	—
Spoon, Medium	All-American (90)	27.95	**100**	**140 B**
	Feature (96)	44.93	—	—
$6.5^L \times 6.5^W \times 8^H$	Regular Line (83-P)	14.95		
Spoon, Small	All-American (90)	23.95	**88**	**110 B**
	Booking (XX-84)	N/A		
	Heartland (88)	23.95		
$5.5^L \times 5.5^W \times 6^H$	Regular Line (88-P)	19.95		
Spring	Easter (87)	25.95	**92**	**115 B**
	Heartland (90-P)	34.95		
	Mother's Day (88)	39.90	**134**	**170 B**
	Regular Line (83-P)	14.95		
$11^L \times 8^W \times 5.5^H$	Woven Traditions (95-P)	41.95		
Star Bound $4.75^L \times 3.75^W \times 2.25^H$	Incentive (95)	N/A	**215**	**300 B**

KEY: * Market Values listed are the AVG and the HIGH Market Values.
C = Combo, **P** = with Protector, **L** = with Liner, **(-P)** = to present

Page in Guide	Form No.	Other Baskets Using Same Form
page 76	1600-DST	Large Hamper
page 76	1700-DST	Medium Hamper, Small Hamper, Medium Waste, 90-91 Recruit
page 76	10162	90 Bee, Poinsettia, 7" Hanging, 7" Measuring, Maple Leaf, 7" Canister
page 76	unknown	88 Employee Birthday, 89 Inaugural 92 Employee Christmas, 92 Recruit, 5" Hanging, Forget-Me-Not, Resolution, 5" Measuring
page 76	13323	Be Mine, 92 Regional Sponsored Award, Small Oval, 97 Small Easter, Rose Petal
page 76	unknown	94 Hostess Appreciation, Lavender, 93 Recruit, Rose Bud
page 76	unknown	Medium Peg, Carry-Along, Small Spoon, Bittersweet, Shaker Peg
page 14 page 60 checklist	11000-OBRS 16349/22/31 11169/11000-OO	94 Bee, Large Peg
page 14 page 24 checklist, HL checklist	10000-OBRS 10000-OO 11096/10000-OCS 11088 /10000-OO	Medium Peg, Bittersweet, Carry-Along, Shaker Peg, 96 Sponsor
page 42 checklist, HL page 100 checklist checklist, WT	900-AX 10936/ 900-AC 900-APS 10928 / 900-AO 10936	91-P Bee Speaker, Bob and Dolores Hope, Boo Basket, 91 Customer Easter, Medium Purse, Red Pottery Thank You, 96 Statehouse
page 88	unknown	Business Card

KEY: In green = Not pictured in the Guide.
HL = Heartland® Collection, **WT** = Woven Traditions®, **R** = Red, **G** = Green

Basket	Collection (Year)	Original Price	Market Values*	
Star Team	Incentive (95)	N/A	**219**	**300 B**
7^L x 5^W x 3.5^H				
Statehouse	Special Event (96)	N/A	—	—
11^L x 8^W x 5.5^H				
Stitching 7RD x 3^H	All-American (89)	25.95	**119**	**155 B**
Sugar and Spice	Booking (88)	N/A	**57**	**75 B**
5.75^L x 3.75^W x 3^H				
Sunburst 22RD	Booking (80)	3.95	**115**	**150**
Summertime 7.75^L x 4.5^W x 2.25^{FH} x 4.5^{BH}	All-American (96)	44.95	**60**	**75 B**
Sweet Basil	Booking (92-94)	22.95	**48**	**65 C**
5^L x 5^W x 2.5^H				
Sweet Pea 8.25^{RD} x 7^H	May (96)	59.95	**76**	**100 C**
Sweet Sentiments 4.25^L x 4.25^W x 3^H	Sweetheart (95)	33.95	**65**	**125 C**
Sweetheart (1990)	Employee Birthday (89)	N/A	**76**	**95 B**
	Sweetheart (90)	32.95	**109**	**145 L**
5.75^L x 3.75^W x 3^H				
Sweetheart (1993)	Sweetheart (93)	29.95	**76**	**175 C**
5^L x 5^W x 2.5^H				

KEY: * Market Values listed are the AVG and the HIGH Market Values.
C = Combo, **P** = with Protector, **L** = with Liner, **(-P)** = to present

Page in Guide	Form No.	Other Baskets Using Same Form
page 88	unknown	Acorn, Basket of Thanks, Tea, Mini Berry, Mini Chore, Mistletoe, Mini Cradle, Baby Easter, Patriot, 91 Hostess Easter, 93 Small Easter, 94 Employee Christmas, Kiddie Purse, Small Key
page 120	900-	91-P Bee Speaker, Bob and Dolores Hope, Boo Basket, 91 Customer Easter, Medium Purse, Red Pottery Thank You, Spring
page 14	5400-ABRS	93 Employee Christmas, Button, Cookie, Show Star
page 24	45000-AO	All-Star Trio, 89 Employee Birthday, Keepsake, Paint the Town, 90 Recruit, Reach for the Stars (Med), Rosemary, 90 Sweetheart, Treasure Chest, 95 Horizon of Hope
page 24	7000-O	None
page 16	18911	None
page 24	10146	90 Employee Birthday, Potpourri, 88-89 Recruit, 93 Regional Sponsored Award, Shamrock, 93 Sweetheart
page 97	14915	None
page 124	19046	None
page 48 page 124	45000- 45000-ARS	All-Star Trio, Keepsake, Paint the Town, 90 Recruit, Shining Star, Rosemary, Sugar and Spice, Treasure Chest, 95 Horizon of Hope
page 124	11347	90 Employee Birthday, Potpourri, Shamrock, Sweet Basil, 93 Regional Sponsored Award, 88-89 Recruit

KEY: In green = Not pictured in the Guide.
HL = Heartland® Collection, **WT** = Woven Traditions®, **R** = Red, **G** = Green

Basket	Collection(Year)	Original Price	Market Values*	
Tea	Employee Christmas (94)	N/A	**93**	**120 B**
	Regular Line (79-P)	7.95		
	Woven Traditions (95-P)	28.95		
7^L x 5^W x 3.5^H				
Tenth Anniversary (1977-87) 15^L x 10^W x 7.5^H	Incentive (87)	N/A	**262**	**320 B**
Thyme 4.5^{RD} x 3^H	Regular Line (95-P)	25.95		
Timeless Memory 11.25^L x 9.25^W x 5.75^H	Mother's Day (97)	69.95	—	—
Tissue	Father's Day (94)	39.95	**90**	**110 C**
6.5^L x 6.5^W x 6.25^H	Regular Line (96-P)	31.95		
Top Performer 10.5^L x 9^W x 8^H	Incentive (92-94)	N/A	**	**
Tour	Employee Birthday (92)	N/A	**62**	**85 B**
	Tour Baskets (88-P)	**	**	**
8.75^L x 4.75^W x 6.5^H				
Tour II 7^L x 3.5^W x 4.75^H	Tour Baskets (96-P)	**	**	**
Tray 14^L x 9^W x 4.5^H	Holiday Hostess (87)	32.95	**109**	**185 B**
Treasure Chest	Incentive (92)	N/A	**197**	**275 B**
5.75^L x 3.75^W x 3^H				
Tree-Trimming 12.5^{RD} x 13.5^H	Holiday Hostess (91)	79.95	**275**	**300 P**
Tulip 14.25^L x 6.25^W x 3.25^H	May (95)	54.95	**83**	**125 C**
Two-Pie 12^L x 12^W x 10^H	J.W. Collection (86)	34.95	**480**	**650 B**

KEY: * Market Values listed are the AVG and the HIGH Market Values.
C = Combo, **P** = with Protector, **L** = with Liner, **(-P)** = to present

Page in Guide	Form No.	Other Baskets Using Same Form
page 50 checklist checklist, WT	700- 10740 /700-JO 10710	Acorn, Basket of Thanks, Mini Berry, Mini Chore, Mistletoe, Mini Cradle, Baby Easter, Patriot, 91 Hostess Easter, 93 Small Easter, Kiddie Purse, Star Team, Small Key
page 82	500-A	88 Bee Speaker, Heirloom, Medium Market, 87 Employee Christmas
checklist	19003	Gold Nugget
page 100	63029	None
page 54 checklist	18490 15831	None
page 86, 88	unknown	Weekender, Remembrance
page 48 page 128	10022 5600-BO	89 Bee, Junior, Sophomore and Senior Recognition, Memory, Flag, Hartville Basket, Dresden Basket
page 128	15814	None
page 68	2300-JGRS	Advisor Recognition, Small Gathering, 92 Bee, 90 Employee Christmas, Pantry
page 86	45000-	All-Star Trio, 89 Employee Birthday, Keepsake, Paint the Town, 90 Recruit, Shining Star, Rosemary, Sugar and Spice, 90 Sweetheart, 95 Horizon of Hope
page 68	1900-BRGS	Banker's Waste, Master Employee, Waste (Inverted, Small Round)
page 97	14648	None
page 92	4800-BT	None

KEY: In green = Not pictured in the Guide.
HL = Heartland® Collection, **WT** = Woven Traditions®, **R** = Red, **G** = Green

Basket	Collection(Year)	Original Price	Market Values*	
Two-Quart	All-American (91)	39.95	**110**	**155 C**
	Feature (85, 87)	28.95	**74**	**80 B**
9.5^{L} x 5^{W} x 9.5^{H}				
Umbrella	J.W. Collection (94)	79.95	**150**	**250 C**
	Retired (79-94)	18.95	**124**	**160 B**
10RD x 17.5^{H}				
Vegetable, Large	Feature (96)	72.43	—	—
	Regular Line (87-P)	26.95		
16^{L} x 9^{W} x 3.5^{FH} x 9^{BH}				
Vegetable, Medium	Regular Line (83-P)	14.95		
	Retired(Natrl) (94)	38.95	**40**	**65 B**
13^{L} x 7.5^{W} x 3^{FH} x 8^{BH}				
Vegetable, Small	Shades of Autumn (90)	35.95	**211**	**295 B**
	Regular Line (83-P)	12.95		
	Woven Traditions (95-P)	35.95		
10.5^{L} x 6.5^{W} x 3^{FH} x 7^{BH}				
Violet	May (90)	34.95	**238**	**375 C**
5^{L} x 5^{W} x 4.5^{H}				
hol Baskets	Incentive (86-P)	N/A	**	**
12^{L} x 7^{W} x 10^{H}				
Waste, Inverted Large Round	Feature (87)	59.95	**124**	**150 B**
	Retired(no/h) (79-84)	26.95	**85**	**110 B**
14RD x 16^{H}	Retired(1sw/h) (79-84)	28.95	**114**	**120 B**
Waste, Inverted Small Round	Retired(no/h) (79-84)	21.95	**90**	**100 B**
	Retired(1sw/h) (79-84)	23.95	—	—
12.5^{RD} x 13.5^{H}				
Waste, Medium (or Large Waste)	Regular Line (79-P)	21.95		
13.5^{L} x 13.5^{L} x 16^{H}				
Waste, Mini	All-American (90)	35.95	**130**	**170 B**
	Father's Day (95)	49.95	**82**	**135 C**
7.5^{L} x 7.5^{W} x 10^{H}	Regular Line (83-P)	18.95		
Waste, Small	All-American (90)	45.95	**138**	**200 B**
	J.W. Collection (84)	34.95	**1031**	**1300 B**
9.5^{L} x 9.5^{W} x 12^{H}	Regular Line (79-P)	16.95		

KEY: * Market Values listed are the AVG and the HIGH Market Values.
C = Combo, **P** = with Protector, **L** = with Liner, **(-P)** = to present

Page in Guide	Form No.	Other Baskets Using Same Form
page 14 page 60	1000-CBRS 1000-CO	91 Employee Christmas, MBA, Tall Key, Tall Purse, Collectors Club Membership
page 92 page 114	11215 11207 /1200-OO	None
page 60 checklist	16543/27/35 15202 /5200-CO	Large Wine
checklist page 114	15105/5100-CO 15113	Yuletide Traditions
page 116 checklist checklist, WT	5000-CGUBS 15008 /5000-OO 15016	None
page 97	14000-BVS	93 Inaugural, Candy Cane, Small Peg, Tea Spoon
page 78, 80	unknown	None
page 62 page 110 page 110	2000-BO 2000-OO 2000-BO	None
page 110 page 110	1900-OO 1900-BO	Banker's Waste, Master Employee, Tree Trimming
checklist	11703	None
page 14 page 54 checklist	12000-OBRS 11266 11258/12000-OO	None
page 14 page 92 checklist	1800-OBRS 1800-OT 11801 /1800-OO	None

KEY: In green = Not pictured in the Guide.
HL = Heartland® Collection, **WT** = Woven Traditions®, **R** = Red, **G** = Green

Basket	Collection(Year)	Original Price	Market Values*	
Waste, Small Miniature 3.75L x 3.75W x 4.75H	Collectors Club (97)	116.85	**232**	**310 C**
Weekender 10.5L x 9W x 8H	Feature (87-88)	54.95	**155**	**170 B**
	Holiday Hostess (88)	65.95	**183**	**225 B**
Wildflower 13.5RD x 8.5H	Regular Line (92-P)	64.95		
Wine, Large 16L x 9W x 3.5FH x 9BH	Retired (83-86)	29.95	**91**	**120 B**
Yuletide Traditions 13L x 7.5W x 3FH x 8BH	Christmas (91)	59.85	**110**	**140 C**
Yuletide Treasures 13.75L x 20.25W x 7.5H	Holiday Hostess (96)	199.95		

KEY: * Market Values listed are the AVG and the HIGH Market Values.
C = Combo, **P** = with Protector, **L** = with Liner, **(-P)** = to present

Page in Guide	Form No.	Other Baskets Using Same Form
page 32	17797	None
page 62 page 68	200-YO 200-YRGS	Remembrance, Top Performer
checklist, Hostess	10111	None
page 114	5200-CO	Large Vegetable
page 28	5100-CRST/CGST	Medium Vegetable
page 70	18627	None

KEY: In green = Not pictured in the Guide.
HL = Heartland® Collection, **WT** = Woven Traditions®, **R** = Red, **G** = Green

Dimensional Search

How To Use:

Many collectors are not always able to identify their baskets. This reference tool was designed to help you determine which basket you may have by looking at its dimensions.

Step 1

Measure your basket. At the top, measure length and width. If round, measure the diameter across the basket. Next, measure its height. All measurements in this Guide are listed in standard form: **Length(L) x Width(W) x Height(H).** Baskets that are sloped will have both its front height **(FH)** and its back height **(BH)** listed.

Step 2

Go to the shape section that your basket most closely resembles. The dimensions are in numerical order. Scan down the list to find your dimension. Because these baskets are individually handmade, measurements may vary within a 1/2". Locate the measurement that is ***closest*** to your basket.

Step 3

Once you have located your basket's dimensions, note the basket name and page number adjacent to it. Refer to that page number in the ***"Quick Find"*** section. The ***"Quick Find"*** will tell you:

(1) . . . the different collection in which your basket has been featured. Now is a good time to note distinguishing characteristics of your basket, such as color weaving or commemorative tags that may point you to a specific collection or series. . .
(2) . . . other baskets that use the same form. . .
(3) . . . its location in the Guide.

If you are still not able to determine which basket you have or have other questions, please feel free to contact us at 1-800-VERIFY IT, ext. 11

Square

Size	Basket	Page
3.75^{L} x 3.75^{W} x 4.75^{H}	See J.W. Miniature Waste	pg. 194
4^{L} x 4^{W} x 4^{H}	See Chives	pg. 146
4.25^{L} x 4.25^{W} x 3^{H}	See Sweet Sentiments	pg. 188
5^{L} x 5^{W} x 2.5^{H}	See Sweet Basil	pg. 188
5^{L} x 5^{W} x 4.5^{H}	See Small Peg	pg. 172
5.5^{L} x 5.5^{W} x 2.5^{H}	See Ivy	pg. 162
5.5^{L} x 5.5^{W} x 6^{H}	See Small Spoon	pg. 186
6.5^{L} x 6.5^{W} x 3^{H}	See Small Berry	pg. 144
6.5^{L} x 6.5^{W} x 6.25^{H}	See Tissue	pg. 188
6.5^{L} x 6.5^{W} x 8^{H}	See Medium Spoon	pg. 186
7.5^{L} x 7.5^{W} x 3.5^{H}	See Medium Berry	pg. 142
7.5^{L} x 7.5^{W} x 10^{H}	See Mini Waste	pg. 192
8.5^{L} x 8.5^{W} x 5^{H}	See Large Berry	pg. 142
8.5^{L} x 8.5^{W} x 7^{H}	See Cranberry	pg. 148
9^{L} x 9^{W} x 4.5^{H}	See Bayberry	pg. 138
9.5^{L} x 9.5^{W} x 12^{H}	See Small Waste	pg. 192
10.5^{L} x 10.5^{W} x 4.5^{H}	See Mother's Day (92)	pg. 168
12^{L} x 12^{W} x 4^{H}	See Pie	pg. 174
12^{L} x 12^{W} x 6^{H}	See Cake	pg. 144
12^{L} x 12^{W} x 10^{H}	See Two-Pie	pg. 190
12^{L} x 12.25^{W} x 16.25^{H}	See Medium Hamper	pg. 160
13.5^{L} x 13.5^{W} x 16^{H}	See Medium Waste	pg. 192
15^{L} x 15^{W} x 7.5^{H}	See Medium Picnic	pg. 174
15.5^{L} x 15.5^{W} x 12.25^{H}	See Evergreen	pg. 152
16^{L} x 16^{W} x 8^{H}	See Coverlet	pg. 148
16.5^{L} x 16.5^{W} x 21.5^{H}	See Large Hamper	pg. 158
17^{L} x 17^{W} x 22^{H}	See Large Hamper, 95	pg. 158

Rectangle

Size	Basket	Page
4.75^{L} x 3.75^{W} x 2.25^{H}	See Business Card	pg. 144
5.5^{L} x 4^{W} x 4^{H}	See Ambrosia	pg. 138
5.75^{L} x 3.75^{W} x 3^{H}	See Rosemary	pg. 182
5.75^{L} x 4^{W} x 3^{H}	See Market, Miniature	pg. 168
6.75^{L} x 4.75^{W} x 2.25^{H}	See Horizon of Hope (96)	pg. 162
6.75^{L} x 9.25^{W} x 3.75^{H}	See Mother's Day (94)	pg. 170
7^{L} x 3.5^{W} x 4.75^{H}	See Tour II	pg. 190
7^{L} x 5^{W} x 3.5^{H}	See Tea	pg. 190

[continued next page]

Rectangle

[continued next page]

Rectangle

Round

[continued next page]

Round

Oval

Additional Basket Information

Additional Basket Informatior

Additional Basket Information